CATALYST

BOOK ONE OF THE CAT LADY CHRONICLES

SUSAN DONOVAN & VALERIE MAYHEW

ADOBE COTTAGE MEDIA, LLC.

Catalyst (Book 1 of the *Cat Lady Chronicles*) is a work of fiction. Names, characters, places, and incidents are the products of the author's imagination or are used fictitiously. Any resemblance to actual events, locales, or persons, living or dead, is entirely coincidental.

Cover design: Elizabeth Mackey
Formatted by: Jesse Kimmel-Freeman

Printed in the United States of America

www.catladychronicles.com

CONTENTS

CONTENTS

INTRODUCTION

What goes on inside our brains when we hear the word "shark"? What makes us draw in that quick breath, immediately engaging our fight-or-flight reflexes? It doesn't seem to matter if "shark" is being coupled with another word, creating terms like "loan shark" or "card shark," or if it is indeed referring to that grim apex predator of the sea. We are immediately apprehensive and, peculiarly, both terrified and fascinated at the same time.

This love-hate relationship is universal and has been documented throughout written history. Yet statistics describing mankind's encounters with sharks do not support this mindset. Shark attacks are not a frequent occurrence. The odds of being killed by a shark are approximately one in four million. You are more likely to be struck by lightning or find a gold nugget in a stream than you are to be bitten by a shark. Yet the fear of shark attacks is palpable among the general population. Although man kills about ten million sharks annually, the world average of deaths from shark attack is approximately eight. This is despite millions of humans working, bathing and swimming in oceans around the world. Here in New Jersey, there have been only sixty encounters between humans and sharks within the last 170 years.

There is considerable debate about why humans have this ambivalence toward sharks. Some say it is because the marine ecosystem is so foreign to us, and we have such limited ability to survive in that realm. Others insist that it is due to our misconceptions about the species and our limited knowledge and understanding of their behavior.

The shark, apex predator of the world's oceans. Would you be any less frightened if we renamed it rosebud? *Courtesy of Pixabay.com.*

Although we can't pinpoint the reason, the fear-fascination factor is evident. One only needs to look at the volume of shark-themed books, movies, TV shows, Internet sites, toys and tourists' tchotchkes to see the obsessive yet ambivalent relationship man has with sharks.

Encounters between humans and sharks fall into two categories: those attacks that are provoked and those considered unprovoked. When humans invade the marine ecosystem and attempt to harass, catch or kill a shark, like any other animal, it will respond defensively and in turn become aggressive. Admittedly, sometimes, it is the shark that initiates the encounter. It is unknown if such attacks are merely a case of mistaken identity, where the shark mistakes human appendages as their prey, or if even the trespass of man and boats into their territory is enough for them to go on the attack. Sometimes, however, it seems that the shark and human were both simply in the wrong place at the wrong time.

The accounts presented here describe the sixty shark attacks from 1842 to the present day as documented in the New Jersey Shark Attack File (NJSAF), established in 1998 by coauthor Robert Heyer to investigate all possible incidents of shark attack within New Jersey waters. See the section at the end of the book for more information. These attacks occurred at thirty different

sites along our shores. Although most communities experienced only one such attack, a few are known to have more than one incident. Sea Bright has the dubious distinction of being the New Jersey hub of shark attacks with a walloping ten documented cases.

Included here, too, is new evidence about many of the attacks, as well as further details and the identification of an additional victim of the horrific summer of 1916, when eight shark attacks were reported within a two-week span.

These narratives do not sensationalize the events but also do not skimp on the facts or the gruesome life-altering effects on the victims. They remind us of how out of place we are in the marine ecosystem. At the same time, they entertain us, describing accounts of bravery in the face of danger, as well as man's foibles and foolishness, which so often contributed to these mishaps.

Shark Attacks of the Jersey Shore provides history and adventure. There is success and failure, as well as heartbreak and laughter. These are the accounts of two creatures, both at the top of their respective food chains, and what sometimes occurs when their paths intersect.

CHAPTER 1

1842–1885

JULY 6, 1842

ABSECON, NJSAF #1

The first known attack by a shark along the Jersey shore occurred on July 6, 1842, in Absecon, located in Atlantic County. On that sunny Wednesday, a group of local boys were clamming along the flats during low tide. They nearly had a full bucket of clams when they discovered a shark floundering in about a foot and a half of water.

One boy decided to tease the shark by poking it with a long stick. The shark ignored him for a minute or two but then twisted its mighty body and lunged at the boy, knocking him into the water. Instantly, the shark's jaws sunk into the boy's flesh. He screamed in agony as he attempted to pull away. But it was too late; his mangled left leg dangled uselessly, spewing blood into the water.

His friends tried to help by beating the creature with sticks, but the damage to the leg was severe. It rendered him handicapped for the remainder of his life.

In this case, the humans provoked the frightened animal. It is a simple lesson: it is never wise to harass a shark!

JUNE 11, 1880

SEA BRIGHT, NJSAF #55

Although the summer of 1880 was noteworthy for its cooler than normal temperatures, it would be recalled for a very different reason by commercial fisherman Winifred White. He would look back on that fateful June 11 day when he successfully escaped an attack from a flying shark. *Sharks can't fly*, you say. I wouldn't be so sure of that.

As White recounted his adventure, which he did with great alacrity, he was on his way back to the dock after a day of fishing when the unthinkable happened. It had been a lucrative day at the fishing banks off the coast of Sea Bright. Before dawn, his sail-powered boat and two-man crew had reached the fishing banks, where they joined the fleet of other fishermen. The horizon was dotted with a dozen other vessels scouring the paths where the schools of migrating fish might travel. After several hours, his catch boxes were nearly full, and White decided to head back to the wharf to unload.

Shark sightings had been numerous that entire summer along the Jersey shore. While this certainly did not panic a fisherman, White knew all too well that a shark, even a small one, could cost him money. Not only did the sharks steal the day's catch, but they also often became entangled and damaged expensive fishing nets. Like others, White kept a watchful eye for sharks. If one came too near the fishing fleet, fishermen quickly dispatched it with a hatchet or axe.

White pulled up anchor, raised his sail and headed toward Sea Bright. There was a robust wind offshore, so he knew he would make good time getting back to port. Just as the sail was tied off, a crewman noticed that a large gray shark was following the boat.

The men continued to watch as the beast grew steadily closer and closer to them. Abruptly, the shark became agitated and began not only keeping pace with the boat but also lifting its head out of the water and baring its huge jagged teeth at the crew.

For a moment, the shark seemed to disappear. Then from along the side of the boat, a great gray form burst from the surface. It sailed high over their heads, spraying sea water across the deck. Just as it reached midship, the shark collided headfirst with the main sail. The boat lurched, the mast groaned in protest and the canvas sail gave way under the weight of the shark. The beast plummeted to the deck with a great thump. The sail snapped back into position with a great twang, as the wobbling boat rolled from side to side.

The shark frantically attacked everything within reach. It thrashed about, wildly slamming the deck with its great tail. Giant jagged teeth flashed in the air, biting anything they could. Much of the catch went flying overboard, as the men huddled on the far end of the deck. Captain White, still uncertain of how badly his craft had been damaged, grabbed an axe and quickly dispatched the beast. It was only then that he could inspect to ensure that the sail was miraculously intact and the precious mast was undamaged.

Captain White brought his trophy back to the dock that afternoon, for he had indeed earned the bragging rights as the man who escaped an attack by a flying shark.

JUNE 17, 1880

SEA BRIGHT, NJSAF #54

June 1880 was cooler than normal. Unlike some summers, when the heat and humidity arrived in early June and lasted until September, that month had sustained temperatures only in the high seventies and low eighties. The cooler temperatures were a welcome relief to those who labored outdoors, including the local fishermen.

During that same period, there were constant reports of shark sightings at both local beaches as well as the fishing grounds off Sea Bright. The abnormal number of sharks prowling the local waters concerned the fishermen. Although these sharks were not reported to be man-eaters, they were troublesome, as they frequently stole the fishermen's catches and ruined their nets.

Being a seasoned boat captain, David Longstreet didn't give the reports of sharks much thought as he set out from Oceanic bound for the fishing grounds off Sea Bright. With him that morning was a young deckhand, Albert, who had joined him earlier that spring. As David steered the craft across the bay, Albert prepared their gear for a day of fishing. They were not the first to arrive at the fishing grounds. Several other fishermen were already busy at work. They acknowledged one another with a wave as they passed and then set to their business.

It turned out to be a perfect day to be on the water. The fish were biting, so in a few hours, David and Albert had filled their hold with eight hundred pounds of fresh fish. Anxious to get their catch to market,

David turned the boat toward home and moved away from the fishing fleet. The men were happy and relaxed as they proceeded toward the bay that afternoon.

They were barely underway when Albert noticed a large marine creature following the boat. He thought it was much too large for a dolphin and must surely be a whale. When the more experienced captain saw it, he knew at once it was a shark.

The creature continued to shadow the boat. It didn't seem to gain on the craft, nor did it ever fall far behind. Suddenly, the great beast spurt through the water aiming straight for them. It struck the bottom of the boat full force with its great head. Wood splintered, and a gush of water spewed into the boat. The men gasped in horror as they made eye contact with the giant creature.

For a second, neither shark nor men moved a muscle. Then, with its head protruding through the splintered wooden bottom, the shark began to discern its predicament. When it grasped that it was stuck in the bottom of the boat, it began to shake the craft so violently that David was tossed headfirst into the water. Although it all happened in seconds, he knew he was in danger. There was no time to check for injuries; a fisherman knows when he is in trouble. If he couldn't get back onboard before the shark got itself free, he was a goner.

But that was easier said than done, for the shark continued to thrash about, twirling the boat around and around. It lifted the craft off the surface and smacked it back down again while an ashen Albert held onto the wheel for dear life. Despite the ship bucking and bobbing like a bronco, David managed, after four attempts, to climb back on board.

He barely took more than two breaths before the shark yanked its head from the bottom of the boat. Immediately, sea water poured into the vessel. David could not recall if he had signaled the other fishermen for help or if they came to his rescue on their own. They raced to plug the hole, caulking it as best they could.

Hoping to keep the vessel seaworthy until they could reach the shore, the two fishermen headed for port as fast as they could. They had just caught their breath when Albert bellowed and pointed to the stern. David turned to see that the very same shark was once again in pursuit of his boat. It followed more closely this time, sometimes even swimming alongside the damaged vessel.

David knew that if the shark attacked again, the temporary patch job would not hold. He needed a diversion, something to get the shark's attention

away from his boat. He shouted to Albert to throw some of the day's catch toward the shark. The first toss sailed over the creature's head. But the second landed right in front of him. He devoured the bait with vengeance, swallowing great mouthfuls of fish. The attack ended but only momentarily. The shark was once again trailing the boat. Now he grew even bolder and stayed very near. As Albert threw more and more fish at the behemoth, it gulped them down in a frenzy.

David brought the boat into the bay with the beast close behind. Frantically, Albert threw an entire bucket of fish that landed on and around the agitated creature, which paused momentarily to devour his feast. When they finally reached shore, they looked back to the water, and the shark was nowhere to be seen.

Neither Albert nor David was injured in the fray, but the boat sustained serious damage. And although they had worked hard to bring in eight hundred pounds of fish that day, by the time they weighed their catch, only six hundred pounds remained. The remainder had been a banquet for a most persistent shark.

AUGUST 29, 1884

BAYONNE, RARITAN BAY, NJSAF #2

The summer of 1884 had been particularly unbearable, with ninety-degree temperatures and unrelenting humidity. By the end of August, everyone was seeking relief from the stifling heat of the city. Edward Moore was no exception. Thrilled to have an afternoon free, he hurried to his small boat moored near Bayonne and headed into the Raritan Bay. It was meant to be a relaxing trip, a chance to cool off and feel the ocean breeze in his hair. He wasn't in a hurry, so he rowed slowly beyond the busy channel. Finally, he pulled in the oars and sat gazing back at the shore. As the boat bobbed gently in the water, an occasional wake splashed against the side of the boat, sending a cool misty spray across his face.

Edward dipped his hand into the water and marveled at how cool it felt despite the fact the temperature had not dipped below ninety for several days. Suddenly, he felt a stinging pain and jerked his hand from the water. Staring into the depths, he saw the unmistakable silhouette of a shark. He took one look at his bloody arm and yanked off his shirt, which he used

to stem the flow of blood that was spewing from a jagged laceration that extended from his fingers to his forearm.

History does not record how Edward Moore managed to return to the shore that day. Nor does it tell us anything about his recovery. It is likely that his enthusiasm for boating waned after the encounter. It is certain, however, that he never again casually dipped his hands into the sea, not even on a hot day.

CHAPTER 2

1886–1895

AUGUST 1886

PARKERSTOWN, HIGHLANDS, NJSAF #3

The summer of 1886 was hot. The heat and humidity began in late June and continued well into mid-August. All along the Jersey shore, the elegant Victorian hotels, opulent summer cottages and even the simple boardinghouses were filled with vacationers from New York and New Jersey. Regardless of where visitors were from, everyone was anxious to simply relax and walk along the beach, letting the cool ocean surf wash across their toes. But before the summer of 1886 would end, that very site would be troubled by not one but three vicious shark attacks.

The first of the series of shark attacks occurred in mid-August in the waters near the Highlands–Sea Bright Bridge. At the time, this section of Highlands was known as Parkerstown. Clams were the lifeblood of the small village, as nearly everyone made their living working the clam beds along the estuaries and bay.

The victims of the attack, John Parker and Edward Matthews, were well-known local clammers. They were standing in about four feet of water in the lower part of the Shrewsbury with clam rakes in their hands when they first saw not one but three sharks. Suddenly, the trio of sharks zeroed in on them. The men scrambled onto the boat with a sigh of relief. Feeling they were safe, they paused to watch as the sharks began to circle.

A fishing village since the 1600s, the Parkerstown section of Highlands was the site of three shark attacks in the summer of 1886. *Authors' photo.*

Clamming and fishing remain the lifeblood of this small village that hugs the bluff overlooking Sandy Hook and the Atlantic Ocean. *Authors' photo.*

Suddenly, one shark rammed their small craft with its great snout. The little boat spun sideways across the surface of the water. Before it came to a complete stop, a second shark struck. All the men could do was hold on for dear life as one after another the sharks took turns ramming the wooden vessel. Buckets of clams were tossed through the air into the water. The men began pelting the sharks with large hard clams from their catch but to no avail. Finally, they began to poke and beat on the creatures with their clam rakes until the handles splintered and broke.

Helpless, the men took to the oars and rowed with all their might toward the closest shore. The sharks did not break off their attack until the boat reached the sandy beach. The men returned to Parkerstown without injury, and the trio of ten-foot unfriendly sharks escaped.

MID-AUGUST 1886

HIGHLANDS/MOUTH OF SHREWSBURY RIVER, NJSAF #4

In the days following the attack on the clammers, the *Red Bank Register* was besieged with claims of shark sightings. Bad news travels fast, and indeed, news of a second shark attack less than a week later spread like wildfire across the shore communities. To make matters more frightening, the attack occurred in the same general area as the incident the week before.

But fishermen had to make a living, and the fishing was good, so they went about their business harvesting the plentiful catches of the summer season. Captain Forman White was a well-known commercial fisherman from Red Bank. An experienced captain, he frequently took his boat and crew to the mouth of the estuaries at Sandy Hook Bay where large schools of menhaden, known to us as mossbunkers, could be found. These schools of baitfish could be caught in large numbers by netting and were an important part of his income.

The crew had been working hard all day and was relieved when the captain gave the order to haul in the nets. The wench creaked as it began pulling the great rope webs bulging with small silvery fish. Smiles and laughter spread across the deck of the fishing boat. This meant a good payday.

The laughter was interrupted by a loud bellowing shout. The great wench groaned to a halt. The men ran to the stern and were horrified

to find several large sharks thrashing within the nets. They were massive beasts, at least ten feet long, with huge mouths filled with bloody jagged teeth.

As the men tried to subdue the sharks, their giant teeth ripped apart the bulging grids of rope. The baitfish escaped the net, fleeing into the open waters. Using whatever they could find, the crew began beating on the intruders. Even axes failed to subdue the behemoths. The panic subsided only when the sharks had freed themselves and escaped. They left behind only a few teeth impaled in the side of the boat and the expensive fishing net in shreds. The men stood silently on the deck of the fishing boat. The hull was empty, the net destroyed. There would be no payday today.

The species of the attackers was never identified. The captain referred to them as "man-eaters," which was a popular term used to describe any large shark, especially a bull or great white. Regardless of the attacker's identity, and while no humans were seriously injured, the attack was costly to both the captain and his crew.

LATE AUGUST 1886

HIGHLANDS, MOUTH OF NAVESINK, NJSAF #5

The heat and humidity continued to plague the Jersey shore that final week of August. Thousands flocked to local beaches and waterways in search of a refreshing sea breeze or to cool off in the surf. Despite numerous shark sightings and recent attacks, business was booming. The hotels and beaches were packed, and the waters were filled with schools of fish ready for the fishermen's nets.

Abruptly, the air of joviality was crushed by the news of yet another shark attack along our shores. Once again, the confrontation took place in the very same waters as two previous attacks. But this time, the culprit would not escape.

Four fishermen—James Taylor, Frank Layton, James Parker and Chas Bradley—were braving the heat in their small fishing boat near the mouth of the Navesink within sight of Parkerstown. If any of them had seen a shark that day, no one had mentioned it to the others. At first, all they saw was a mere shadow just beneath the surface of the water as the long dark silhouette slowly but deliberately circled the wooden craft.

This captured the crew's attention, but before anyone could speak, the shark seemed to spurt through the water, ramming into the bottom of the wooden boat. All the men could do was hold on for dear life as the boat raised above the water and then shuddered as it fell back to the surface with a wallop. Water sprayed everywhere, fish toppled out of deck boxes and equipment slid across the deck.

Before the men could collect themselves, the animal was back again, ramming against the side with all its might. Again and again, the attacker returned to battle the small wooden craft. The men grabbed anything they could—axes, gaffs and rakes—and began beating the beast. Despite the shark being outnumbered four to one, it was said to have "put up one heck of a fight." The creature was finally subdued and killed.

The fishermen hauled the seven-foot bull shark back to the shore, reporting that the hardened thick skin was as rough as sandpaper. This was the third shark incident of that summer, and as Labor Day approached, locals and visitors alike expressed relief that at least no one had been seriously injured, well, not unless you happen to have been the shark.

AUGUST 17, 1890

SEA BRIGHT, NJSAF #6

August 1890 found the beaches overflowing with weekend vacationers anxious to escape the grimy stale heat of the city. Arriving by public or private transport, they all were eager to feel the cool salty breezes.

James Whiteside, an importer from Manhattan, was no exception. He was captivated by both boating and especially salt-water fishing. He spent long weekends at the shore. By the summer of 1890, he was a regular at local restaurants and hotels in Sea Bright.

Whiteside was an avid angler and would happily fish for anything. But he especially loved when the blues were running, as they were known to put up such a good fight. On that fateful weekend, he chartered a local fishing boat and arranged for his friends to join him on Sunday for a day of fishing.

It was a perfect day to be out on the water. Although there was a stout breeze, the air was balmy, and the ocean glistened in the bright sunshine. As soon as everyone arrived, the captain cast off, sailing up the inlet and

around the hook, and was soon nearly half a mile offshore near Normandie Beach in Sea Bright.

Whiteside, being quite competitive in nature, was anxious to catch the first blue of the day. In fact, he hoped to bring in the largest bluefish of all. Whiteside shunned a rod and reel, maintaining that a true sportsman used a hand troll to fish. In this method, a baited line, sometimes with several hooks, is thrown overboard and slowly pulled behind the boat. Some fishermen used small pulley devices to pull in the line. But Whiteside used the direct hand method, pulling in the long fishing line with his own two hands. His only tackle was a set of hand protectors known as stalls.

Although the other members of the fishing party knew of their host's strong attitudes about fishing methods, most were using rods and reels. It wasn't very long before they came upon a school of bluefish. Everyone grabbed their gear and instantly began pulling blues onto the boat. One after another, fish after fish was pulled in and lay flopping on the floor of the boat. That was, everyone except Mr. Whiteside. He pulled in his bait and inspected it. Nothing had even nibbled on the piece of squid on the end of his line.

He tried to ignore the cheering of his pals as they battled and caught countless fish. Soon the men began to tease him and offered to lend him their fishing rods. Whiteside grew grumpier and grumpier and even more determined than ever to catch a fish. Suddenly, something jerked the line from his hands. His shriek was part agony and part joy, for although the line was cutting through his rubber stalls and searing his hands, he knew that at last he had caught a large fish.

Whiteside braced himself and held on. He began drawing in the cord, pulling the fish closer and closer. A jerk from the fish nearly knocked him off his feet. He tugged in the great lengths of line, hand over hand, only to have it jerked away as the huge fish fought for its life. After a while, the fish seemed to tire, allowing Whiteside to pull it nearly to the surface.

By now, everyone else had stopped fishing and was watching the battle between Whiteside and his fish. A great yell went out, for James Whiteside had not caught a giant bluefish—he had caught a shark, a very big shark.

The captain ran for his rifle and told Whiteside to hold the shark in place. But the moment he fired the gun, the shark once again nose-dived to the bottom, forcing Whiteside to wrestle it back to the surface.

On the second attempt, the captain fired nearly point blank at the shark. The water around the boat turned crimson, but the shark was not ready to submit. It plummeted toward the bottom, and this time it nearly took

Whiteside with him. No one could say James Whiteside was a quitter. Heaving with all his might, he brought the shark alongside the boat once more. Someone gaffed the creature, and it was finally hauled on board.

A cheer went up. Whiteside had landed the shark! Smiling broadly with pride, he took a steel ruler and was set to measure his trophy. At that moment, the shark raised its tail and slammed the bottom of the wooden boat. Everyone jumped back as the shark continued to hammer the wooden floorboards with its powerful tail.

Excitement turned to horror. The captain was afraid to shoot the shark again for fear of damaging his boat, yet the sound of shattering wood made the passengers fear for their lives. A crewman found some stout rope with which he lassoed the beast's great tail. Once they drew it to a stanchion, the shark was secure. Whiteside measured his catch and found it to be five feet, seven inches long. More quickly than they had brought it aboard, they rolled the shark back into the Atlantic.

There was no serious injury to anyone on the boat that day, although the craft sustained some damage. Everyone had an adventure to share when they got home. James Whiteside maintained his reputation as an avid and talented fisherman. But he emphatically stated that if he ever again caught a shark, he would immediately cut his line.

AUGUST 29, 1891

LONGPORT, NJSAF #7

Folks along the East Coast welcomed the onset of summer in 1891. It had been a particularly cold winter with a February blizzard that left the region paralyzed for over a week. Yet by August 29, the heat was suffocating the Jersey shore.

That Friday evening, the air was stagnant and still. It did little to cool the seasoned crews of the *Mary C. Brown* and the *William Briggs*, two schooners anchored just off Longport, New Jersey. It was nearly twilight, and the crew was trying to catch any bit of breeze possible. The two ships were moored so closely together that the men could call back and forth to one another.

Crews from both ships planned to go ashore that night and visit the pubs. Their conversations were interrupted when the *Mary C. Brown*'s first

A commercial fishing boat of the era proudly displays the day's catch, including the carcass of a lone bycatch shark. *Historical postcard of 1890s, authors' collection.*

mate called out that sharks were prowling around the schooners. The men scurried about the decks trying to catch sight of the intruders.

There was a bit of debate about the situation, which quickly escalated into a few challenges between the crews and even a wager as to who could kill the first shark. Both ships instantly emptied of men as they began lowering the yawls into the water.

Just offshore, they soon came upon a group of about a dozen sharks. Those men with firearms began shooting at the herd, while others used harpoons and gaffs to attack them. Several animals were wounded, and three were killed. They proudly towed the carcasses to shore, where they found their trophies to be between twelve and fifteen feet in length.

The crews were the heroes of the local pubs, and so the remainder of the night was spent drinking and sharing accounts of the adventures with anyone who would listen. One sailor said that a shark made eye contact with him. Another claimed that a shark had intentionally gone for his throat. Above all, the crew members generally agreed that the creatures were bloodthirsty and eager for human flesh.

As the beer flowed, the claims of bravery swelled, and the accounts of the sharks' ferocity escalated. By midnight, the stories were totally unbelievable. But no one seemed to notice. Fueled by the drink, the men decided to go out early in the morning and kill the remainder of the school. Friendly

competition evolved into a lottery of sorts. Everyone contributed to a jackpot that would go to the crew that killed the most sharks.

The next morning, long before the hangovers had worn off, the crews of the *Mary C. Brown* and the *William Briggs* once again lowered their yawls into the early dawn light. This time, they came prepared with guns, extra ammo, harpoons, gaffs and axes. Spirits were high as the men planned to take out the man-eaters once and for all. Although everyone was determined to win the bragging rights for killing the biggest shark, it was never far from anyone's mind that a sizeable jackpot awaited the winners.

The small wooden yawls crammed with sailors and their weapons headed away from the mother ships and moved into open water. They didn't need to go far before they spotted the dorsal fin of a large shark. But it wasn't just one shark; there were dozens hovering close together directly ahead.

No sooner had the cry "Shark!" echoed across the water than the sea suddenly turned a muddy gray as hundreds of angry sharks appeared from nowhere. It was as if they had been lying in wait for the men's arrival. Before the men could react, the herd rushed the small wooden crafts.

While some of the sharks circled the boats, others repeatedly rammed their great heads against the wooden hulls. Within a few minutes, the sound of splintering wood was heard as one after another the huge beasts punched through the bottom of one of the boats, forcing the crew to constantly bail water to keep from sinking into the mass of frenzied creatures. Others fired off as many volleys as they could or stabbed at the sharks with anything they could find.

The well-intentioned plans of the crew were in shambles. Dozens of sharks had encircled their yawls. Others lunged at the men with gaping mouths, exposing their jagged bloody teeth. One flung itself onto the gunwale and took an enormous bite out of one of the crew. The frenzied sharks even chased the panicked sailors' boats as they tried to flee the attack.

It was all the crew could do to bring the limping boats back to the schooners. Although several had suffered bites and cuts, they were relieved to be back aboard their mother ships. When questioned by their respective captains, the crews insisted that before they were chased back to the schooner, they had killed two large man-eaters from the pack.

When word got out about the incident, the locals had a good laugh at the expense of the crew. Although the men were anxious to tell their side of the story and share their personal exploits of bravery, no one went back to the pub to collect the winnings from the shark lottery.

AUGUST 2, 1895

RARITAN BAY, NJSAF #8

It was very unusual for Elias Turner and Jacob Van Hesse to be out on the water on a weekday. Although the two friends loved to go fishing, it was usually restricted to weekends when they either were not working or their wives didn't have plans for them.

When an odd set of coincidences that week created a rare work-free Friday for the pair, they immediately made plans to make the most of the opportunity. The duo arrived at the dock early in the morning with their tackle, thermoses and a basket of sandwiches. Since Elias had broken his right arm a few weeks earlier and it was still in the tightly bound metal and wooden splint, Jacob grabbed the heavier and bulky gear and stowed it on the small boat. In no time at all, they were on their way out into Raritan Bay.

As soon as they reached their favorite fishing spot near Round Shoals, they cast their lines and settled in to wait for a bite. They talked for a while, but as the sun rose and the temperatures increased, they grew quieter. The fish were not biting. About every half hour, each man would reel in his line, inspect his bait and cast it out once again. They had been there over two hours, and neither man had so much as a nibble.

Elias sat at the stern with his left arm resting near the tiller. Sitting nearer to the bow, Jacob leaned slightly forward, concentrating on the surface of the water, willing for movement of his bobber. The breeze was mild, and as the sun grew warmer, Elias's eyes grew heavier and heavier. Finally, he was fast asleep.

Jacob turned to comment but saw that his friend's eyes were closed. He smiled; Elias could rest a few minutes more. But when his pal awoke, Jacob planned to tease him about the giant fish that got away.

As he slept, Elias's right arm, heavy from the weight of the splint, fell from the tiller to his lap. It slid off his thigh until it dangled over the side, with his fingers just touching the water's surface.

Suddenly, the boat jerked sideways, and Jacob heard a fearsome sound. He wasn't sure if it was a gurgle, a choked gasp or even a scream. He spun about just in time to see a giant shark with its teeth embedded in Elias's arm. Before he could speak, the giant mouth yanked his friend into the water.

The first thing that Elias felt was an excruciating pain in his shoulder and elbow. Something with tremendous force clamped down on his splinted arm. By the time he opened his eyes, he was already under water, and his arm felt

The highly aggressive bull shark, *Carcharhinus leucas*, tenacious in its attack, considered by most a man-eater. *www.goodfreephotos.com, Timothy Knepp, U.S. Fish and Wildlife Service.*

like it was in a vice. He tried to breathe, but a foul liquid blocked the air, and his chest burned as if it were on fire.

Meanwhile, Jacob dashed to the side of the boat and peered into the cloudy water. Several yards down, he could see the outline-form of Elias. He ripped off his jacket, grabbed a fish scaler and dove as deeply into the water as he could. At the same moment, Elias was trying to focus on what had entrapped his arm. It was then he came face to face with the bluntnose shark. In desperation, he began to beat on the beast with his free arm.

Jacob rushed at the shark and plunged his knife deep into its side. With his other hand, he grabbed Elias's leg and held on. But the beast would not let go. Jacob gouged the attacker repeatedly until the water was red with blood.

Just then, the shark released its grip. Jacob clutched Elias with one hand and pulled him to the surface. He was still conscious but was barely alert and needed Jacob's help to remain afloat.

With one arm holding Elias, Jacob swam for the boat. They were still not out of danger, and getting them both back on the boat was not going to be easy. Jacob brought his injured friend to the stern where the rudder hangs off the transom. He shoved Elias up onto the overhang, perching him precariously over the water. Then he quickly pulled himself onto the boat and dragged Elias onto the deck.

The two sprawled on the deck, panting and gasping for air. Jacob scanned the horizon; there were no other boaters in sight. He applied a makeshift tourniquet to Elias's arm and headed for Staten Island as quickly as he could. In Tottenville, a local doctor found that Elias's arm was indeed refractured. But it was saved from amputation because the shark could not chew through the metal and wooden splint.

Over the years, the two were often asked about their encounter with the shark. When Elias conveyed the story, he explained how his brave friend saved his life on that fishing trip. When Jacob narrated the account, he spoke of his friend's amazing courage and endurance that enabled him to survive a vicious shark attack. The one thing they both agreed on is that neither would ever again fall asleep on a fishing trip.

1898–1913

JULY 27, 1898

SEA BRIGHT, NJSAF #56

Edward Phillips had much to be grateful for on that warm July morning. Although the sun had not yet risen, he had a good feeling about the day. The air was still cool, the weather looked promising and if he had a few more good days with his lobster traps, he could soon pay off his beloved boat, the *Eleanora*. Like other fishermen of Sea Bright, he sold his catches to the local hotels and restaurants. Business was thriving; Long Branch was a magnet for wealthy New Yorkers and Philadelphians who wanted to escape the heat of the city.

When Edward reached the dock, he saw that his deckhand, a young Swedish lad, had already arrived and had begun preparing the boat for the day's work. The two quickly inspected their bait and wooden lathe lobster pots to ensure they were ready for the day.

The sun was just coming up when they cleared the bay and headed into open water. The *Eleanora* made straight for the spot where they had left their pots the day before. It was a matter of mutual respect and integrity that a lobsterman never bothered another man's pots. To do so would earn him not only the wrath of the victim but also total shunning by the fishing community.

Edward passed the pots of others and made his way to his traps just off Sea Bright. Once they arrived, the work began in earnest. They quickly

pulled up each pot one by one and moved the contents into a rectangular holding box that was filled with sea water.

Each trap was inspected, rebaited and cast off the side of the boat before they moved on to the next. There were dozens to be collected and rebaited. The two worked quickly until every trap was back in place beneath the water. It had been a good catch. The two men shared a smile knowing that today would be a good payday for both.

As they headed back to port, they began to chat, mostly about lobsters and fishing. Edward kept a fishing net on board that he sometimes used to catch whatever might be schooling in the area. They decided to cast the net and see what they could gather as they made their way home.

As they towed the net slowly behind the boat, Edward began telling the lad stories about lobstering. The young man couldn't believe that at one time lobsters were not considered fit for human consumption and that only the very poor ate them, as they were primarily used for animal fodder.

Just then, the boat seemed to quiver and lunge toward the stern. The men raced to inspect the net. They began hauling it in as quickly as they could, but the weight was tremendous. The contents of the net seemed to thrash from side to side and then would suddenly plummet toward the bottom, dragging the net off the spindle. They yanked on the net with all their strength. At last, a great grayish form emerged from the dark water. It was a shark.

The beast was not at all what they wanted to catch, but it was tangled in the netting and could not escape. Although it heaved its great body in every direction and attacked the nets with huge jagged teeth, it was trapped. Fearing that the shark would destroy the fishing net, the two hammered on the creature's head with whatever they could find until it was finally subdued. At last, the huge shark lay motionless within the mass of tangled netting.

They fastened the ensnared creature to the side of the boat and headed for shore. Time was of the essence. The lobsters had to be delivered immediately while they were still alive; freeing the shark would have to wait.

Just as they neared the lobster delivery wharf, the shark suddenly came back to life. The boat seemed to be suspended in air for a second, and then it wobbled and rotated slightly. The frenzied beast thrashed about, spraying water across the deck. Its huge mouth filled with rows of jagged teeth aimed for the two fishermen. Edward grabbed an axe and dispatched the creature once and for all. With the bloody carcass still attached to the boat, the *Eleanora* quickly delivered its catch of fresh lobsters. Then and only then did it proceed to its home dock, where the shark was removed from its entrapment.

JULY 6, 1902

ATLANTIC CITY, NJSAF #9

The Fourth of July was celebrated in grand style in Atlantic City in 1902. Both local citizens and visitors alike would say, and why not? The resort was at the peak of its success. Great hotels, elegant restaurants and amusements dotted the city. Society's darlings came here to eat, drink and play. Starlets, athletes, industrialists and politicians basked in elaborate cabanas on the wide sandy shores of Atlantic City.

Beaches were filled with the well-heeled clad in the latest bathing costumes. Genteel ladies of fashion rode in rolling chairs along the boardwalk, and children vied for tissue-wrapped logs of saltwater candy. New mechanical amusement rides, including the brand-new Loop-de-Loop, drew throngs of families to the shore. It is not a surprise that Atlantic City celebrated that Fourth of July in grand style, complete with parades, parties and fireworks.

Bad news came with the Sunday edition of the *New York Times*: a man had been severely bitten while bathing on an Atlantic City beach. The newspaper identified the victim as Harry M. Speerman. According to the press account, the victim was swimming not far from Steeple Chase Pier. Having swum nearly a quarter of a mile into the ocean, he turned and began his leisurely trip back to the shore. When he was halfway to the beach, he saw a dark form in the water.

At first, he thought it was another swimmer, but the figure didn't seem to be moving on its own. Thinking it was a drowning victim or possibly even a corpse, he increased his speed, and as he approached, he reached out and grabbed ahold of the floating rubble.

But Harry wasn't holding on to a drowning victim or even a corpse; he had grabbed the tail of a shark. He saw his error immediately, but it was too late. The shark lurched from his grasp, whirled about and attempted to latch on to Harry's left foot. Dodging the attack, Harry began swimming toward the beach as quickly as he could. The shark, which was in close pursuit, was not about to give up. It lunged at its prey, its giant teeth ripping the flesh from Harry's left arm and turning the water red with his blood.

The lifeguards saw the struggle and rushed to his aid. Armed with harpoons and a boat hook, they quickly dispatched the predator. Harry Speerman received medical care, and although his arm was severely damaged, it did not require amputation. It remains a mystery what species of shark attacked Harry that day.

Atlantic City beaches, protected by elevated lifeguard stations, welcomed visitors in full dress as well as the latest bathing costumes of the day. *Historical photo, authors' collection.*

But the mystery does not end there. Even today, some 115 years later, we may not have truly identified the victim at all. Newspapers that reported the event all identified the injured man as Harry M. Speerman. Both the *New York Times* and the Fort Wayne paper described him as a Midwest native who had arrived in Atlantic City only the day before the accident. Yet when the Fort Wayne press investigated further, it could find no record of anyone by that name living in the vicinity.

At the same time, others asserted that the victim was a local man who worked as a baker. Searches for a local baker named Harry Speerman were fruitless. So the mystery remains, who was the man who grabbed a shark by its tail and lived to tell the tale? And why didn't he do so?

SEPTEMBER 16, 1903

ATLANTIC CITY, NJSAF #10

The Reverend John McMillan, pastor of the Atlantic City Presbyterian Church, was a friendly and outgoing man. Most of his days were busy. He did everything from church maintenance, to writing and delivering sermons, to baptizing babies, to performing weddings and funerals. He even had the unenviable task of settling disputes between the ladies of the altar guild. It left him little time for hobbies or recreation.

In early September, Charles Tull, a longtime parishioner, invited Reverend McMillan to join him and some colleagues for a midweek afternoon of fishing. Tull had just purchased a new boat, the *Anna M*, and was eager for a day on the water with some friends. Reverend McMillan was delighted by the invitation. He didn't get many opportunities to spend an entire afternoon away from his duties, especially one that meant a day of fishing.

The weather was perfect that September day. The sun was shining, the waters were calm and the temperature made it feel more like June than September. Everyone clambered aboard and stowed their poles and tackle on deck. Within a few minutes, Tull was piloting the boat away from the dock and heading toward the horizon. Once away from the marina, he set course for his favorite fishing spot, a grassy bay several miles away.

About forty minutes into the trip, Tull slowed the *Anna M* and gingerly entered the small shallow bay, which was protected from the open ocean by a narrow grassy marsh. Tull dropped anchor, allowing the *Anna M* to bob gently on the glistening, clear water.

The men wasted no time grabbing their tackle and setting up their poles for fishing. Within minutes, their lines were cast and competition for the first catch began. The pastor looked out from the stern, tracing his line from the pole until it disappeared into the water. Suddenly, he felt a strong yank on his line as his pole bent toward the water. He grabbed the rod more tightly and jerked it upward, trying to set the hook, and began to reel in his catch. Although the others cheered him on, he was soon unable to turn the crank on the reel any further. There was no doubt that the reverend had caught something very large. The pastor was holding his rod with one hand as he leaned over the side to catch sight of the fish when he lost his balance and went headfirst into the water with a giant splash. The brief chuckle that spread around the deck was interrupted by the cry of "Shark!"

As the reverend dropped into the water, the dark beast charged at him with a gaping mouth of exposed jagged teeth. The clergyman dove to escape the attack, but the shark followed. Giant teeth penetrated his shoulder, leaving a large bloody wound, which spewed a cloud of blood into the water.

In panic, he heaved himself to the surface, with the beast in pursuit. But as the shark went in for the kill, it was met by the sharpened prong of a boat hook and the repeated assaults by an axe and gaffs by the fishermen. Within minutes, the shark floundered several yards away in a pool of crimson water.

The pastor was quickly brought onboard. Although he received several ugly lacerations, his bleeding was contained. Meanwhile, two of the men tied the creature to the boat. The *Anna M* hurried to shore with the shark in tow. Once there, it was measured and found to be nine feet in length.

The Reverend McMillan recovered from his injuries, although they left ugly scars on his shoulder and arm. More than one friend reminded him

that when a clergyman falls into the sea, he should be looking for a whale, like Jonah, not a man-eating shark. The pastor was a good sport about it all. But everyone agreed, without a doubt, that the reverend had a guardian angel watching over him that day.

JULY 28, 1904

NAVESINK RIVER, NJSAF #11

Things were bustling along the Jersey shore that final week of July 1904. "No Vacancy" signs appeared at local hotels and boardinghouses, and crowds jammed the beaches and local restaurants. The weather was beautiful and the setting nothing short of picturesque. These very things brought two business associates, Mr. Schmidt and Dr. Oakley, to Sea Bright for a long weekend.

The two avid sailing enthusiasts planned to complete some unfinished contract matters and then cruise the Shrewsbury and Navesink Rivers aboard a chartered sailboat. They arrived by the noon train and settled in their rooms at the luxurious Normandie Hotel in Sea Bright. The rambling three-story wooden structure faced the ocean, providing its guests with a constant sea breeze. The rear of the building was nestled against the Shrewsbury River with a long narrow wharf that ran the length of the property.

By dinnertime, they had completed their business and headed to the dining room for a seafood dinner to celebrate their success. Over a leisurely feast of lobsters and chowder, they discussed their plans for the remainder of the weekend. The sailboat had been hired and picnic hampers and charts secured for local waters. The remainder of the weekend would be for relaxation.

Early the next morning, attired in their colorful sailing blazers, they met for breakfast on the veranda of the hotel. They picked up their hamper from the main desk and headed out to the dock.

Once on board, they inspected the fittings and sails of the small sailboat. They agreed that everything was in order. Schmidt undid the lines and unfastened the sail bindings. They rowed away from the dock until they were nearly midstream in the inlet, allowing the current to carry them until they reached the mouth of the Navesink.

With Dr. Oakley at the helm and Schmidt manning the sails, the little craft eased into the approach to the river. Phragmite-covered sedge islands

Known for its luxurious accommodations and fine dining, the Normandie Hotel was a premier destination in Sea Bright for the well-heeled. *Courtesy of Mark Leckstein, Sea Bright Historical Images on Facebook.*

led the way, and soon they were sailing within the channel of the Navesink. The doctor steered the boat carefully while Schmidt tied in the jib and then moved back to the mainsail. He adjusted it until they caught the breeze, and the craft began gliding up the river.

The two men were chatting amicably, discussing the picturesque landscape. Schmidt had just begun to remind Oakley about the New York Subway opening that weekend when he saw a long dark form in the water. It wasn't until they realized it was keeping pace with them that they slowed down to get a better look at their visitor.

It was Oakley who first identified it as a shark, although neither expected to find such a large animal in these brackish waters. It suddenly became agitated, swimming rapidly from one side of the boat to the other. It would disappear into the depths, appearing suddenly to port and then appear at the stern. One moment it would be several yards off starboard, and in the next moment it was swimming rapidly only inches from the gunwale.

The men adjusted the sails, trying to catch more wind and escape the pursuer. But it was no use; the shark came closer and closer. Suddenly, it rammed the boat, hitting the keel with its great head. The boat ricocheted violently as the boom swung across the deck. The men scrambled to control the craft as the shark once again butted the side of the boat.

Fearful that it would capsize them, Oakley grabbed an oar. As their attacker made its third pass, he beat on the creature with the blade until it cracked and broke into pieces. At that moment, the shark lunged for deeper waters, and Dr. Oakley lost his balance and fell into the river.

Horrified, Schmidt raced to the side. He reached into the water and yanked his friend back on board before the shark could return. Although wet and frightened, Dr. Oakley was unhurt. It was only then that the men regained control of the boat. Slightly bruised and frightened, the two men turned and made way for Sea Bright.

They returned to the dock with their uneaten hamper, empty flasks and broken oars. After relaying the incident to the dock master, they proceeded directly to the hotel bar for the first of many tall gimlets.

LATE AUGUST 1905

ATLANTIC CITY, NJSAF #12

Late August 1905 felt like most late August days in Atlantic City. It was hot, humid and hazy. Although September was only a few days away, there was no hint of cooling temperatures or the coming of autumn leaves.

George Wright, a stockbroker from Pittsburgh, was spending a fortnight in Atlantic City. Although the financial world was his business, athleticism was his avocation. George loved exercise and sports of all kinds. He was an excellent swimmer and especially loved the challenge of ocean swimming. Although he swam daily off the beach in Atlantic City, he took any opportunity he could to swim in the deeper offshore waters. George admitted that swimming in deeper waters could be dangerous and somewhat challenging. Yet he insisted that it was the most wonderful form of swimming, one you had to experience to appreciate.

When George woke that morning, the air was already stagnant. He smiled to himself, pleased with his foresight to charter the boat for the fishing trip today. Not only would there be great fishing at the grounds farther from the beach, but there would be cooler, fresher air. And if he had time, he might do a bit of deep-water swimming in the offshore waters.

George had invited a few friends to join him when he arranged to hire a twenty-six-foot naphtha boat for the day. The captain and his two-man crew were experienced fishermen who knew the local waters well. George had no doubt that the fishing expedition would be a success.

They set off early that morning, and by the time most people were eating their breakfast, they had arrived at the fishing banks off the shore of Atlantic City. It was an amiable group. There was good-natured teasing and laughter as every fisherman managed to haul in several good-sized fish.

They had just finished for the day and the captain was preparing to return to shore when George asked him to wait for a few minutes while he took a dip in the deeper ocean waters. Although George invited his guests to join him in the swim, everyone declined. George stripped to his swim trunks,

walked to the side and dived into glistening blue water. He had not been in the water very long before the captain spied several dark silhouettes moving in their direction. He motioned to George to return to the boat.

At first, George began his return in a leisurely fashion, savoring each moment of his swim. Then the captain's beckoning became frantic, for the sharks were only a hundred yards away. The captain started the engine and moved toward George, who by now sensed the danger and was swimming as fast as he could toward the boat.

He was only yards away with the sharks close behind. The captain killed the engine and grabbed a flare gun and shot directly into the leading shark, dispatching it instantly. As he continued shooting at the beasts, the others pulled the exhausted swimmer back on board and then tried to stem the flow of blood that was gushing from his foot where he once had toes.

The captain raced back to shore with his injured passenger. Although George walked with a bit of a limp the remainder of his life, he suffered no other effects from the shark bite. It didn't quell his devotion to swimming at all. By the next summer, his wounds were healed, and George was back out in the ocean, swimming in the deep water.

AUGUST 8, 1907

LOWER DELAWARE BAY, NJSAF #13

Who would think that the *Crassostrea virginica*, the tiny eastern oyster, harvested along our bays and estuaries for so many years, could possibly be involved in a violent encounter between a man and a shark?

All along the Jersey shore, the estuaries and inlets have been home to the natural beds of eastern oysters for hundreds of years. Although most natural sites were depleted many years ago, a remaining site in Delaware Bay was frequented by many locals, including the Kell brothers of Bridgeton. Although not commercial oystermen, the three brothers knew the waters well and had an enterprising spirit. Like his two brothers, George held down a full-time job, planted a large truck patch of vegetables for the local farm market and frequently harvested oysters in the nearby bay.

The three had grown up on the Cohansey River in Bridgeton and knew the river and tide cycle by heart. Time and again they carefully planned trips to the oyster beds to be sure that the outgoing tide swept them easily

downstream to the bay. The timing had to be perfect, for it also had to be the period when the oyster beds were accessible, with the tidal level shallow enough for them to stand in the water and use their rakes but deep enough to float the boat. George was a master of this calculation, although his brothers claimed he was just lucky.

On August 8, the three left the dock at the tail end of the outgoing tide. It wasn't long before they arrived at the "drum beds" located about a mile offshore. It was a large field of natural oysters about a half mile long and a quarter mile wide. They floated the boat over the bed until they found a promising site where they dropped a small anchor. Using twine, they secured a large wicker basket into position in the center of the rowboat to hold the day's catch.

The brothers gently eased themselves over the side of the boat into the bay where the water reached just above their waists. They pulled their long-handled oyster rakes from the boat and set to work scouring the bottom for the precious mollusks.

The basket began to fill quickly as the men repeatedly pulled the rakes across the sandy bottom and then pulled them upward to reveal their catch of a half dozen or so oysters. These were quickly deposited into the basket, and the men returned to their raking.

George had just yanked his rake upward out of the water and leaned forward to examine an assortment of small oysters on his rake when he was sideswiped by a large dark form that knocked him off his feet. He tumbled into the water but quickly regained his footing. He stood there with his hand on his chest staring at the water.

His brothers witnessed the shark attack and knew they were in danger. They rushed to George's side, rakes in hand, ready when the shark turned back and raced toward George. The two hammered on the animal relentlessly, all the while shouting at George to get into the boat.

George flung himself into the stern, still holding his chest. As the shark fled from its attackers, the brothers quickly climbed aboard. Seeing that George had a large graze mark across his torso, they made straight for shore. Although the rowing was more difficult going upstream that time of day, they never slowed down until they reached the outskirts of Bridgeton.

George recovered completely from the attack. He was treated for the sizable abrasion across his chest, which his brothers affectionately referred to as Georgie's shark kiss.

AUGUST 27, 1913

SPRING LAKE, NJSAF #14

Spring Lake, New Jersey, has played host to the rich and famous since the 1890s. Robber barons, socialites, politicians and Hollywood starlets have all spent summers in the elegant homes and palatial cottages that line the shore. August 1913 found the municipality filled with these posh summer visitors.

Although you would never know it by their public persona, more than a few of them were more than unhappy about the recent passage of the Sixteenth Amendment to the Constitution, which enabled the federal government to impose an income tax on all individuals in the United States. Although it was too early to know how that would affect their assets, even the wealthy cast a wary eye on the legislation.

For the crew of the fishing boat moored about a mile off the coast of Spring Lake, the only thing on their minds was fish, or lack thereof. Although the morning seemed perfect for a day on the water, the fish seemed to be a bit reluctant about biting. On board the fishing boat, in addition to the crew, was a group of tourists, some trying their hand at deep-sea fishing for the first time. They kept the crew busy helping them untangle their lines or bait their hooks.

Standing farther away from their commotion were several more experienced fishermen who had brought their own gear and required little assistance from the crew. Among them was William Ohmer of Dayton, Ohio, who, although a summer resident himself, was practically a regular on the daylong fishing trips. He came as often as three times a week to try his luck with his personal saltwater tackle and rod.

By midday, the fishing had improved, and soon even the novices had caught at least one fish. Suddenly, the man standing beside Ohmer felt the line being ripped from his reel. He grabbed the pole with both hands and jerked upward and immediately began reeling in his catch. The tourists looked on in awe as the fisherman battled the invisible creature.

A crew member ran to assist, standing by with a net. Finally, the catch was brought to the surface. The crewman's eyes widened, and he dropped the net and grabbed a harpoon, which he thrust into the shark. The creature floundered in the water for a time and then was still. Only when they were certain that it was dead did they drag it onboard.

The remainder of the trip was unnoteworthy. The vacationers stared at the huge carcass while the fishermen talked quietly among themselves,

Tourists may be terrified of a shark in the wild but eagerly pose with captured specimens as a memento of their trip. *Historical postcard, "Mr. Sharky," authors' collection.*

repeatedly measuring and inspecting the carcass. When they docked, the tourists grabbed their souvenir fish and hurried away.

The locals took more time in clearing up their gear. They watched as the crew dressed the shark, removing the tail and head. Then they cut into the torso, attempting to slice it lengthwise. The internal organs looked normal except for the stomach, which was misshapen and bloated. The fishermen sliced across the distended organ with a filet knife and peeled it open. There, among some partially digested food, was a human foot. The foot was wearing a woman's tan-colored shoe and the remainder of a knitted stocking. There was nothing else in the shark that could help identify the foot's owner, nor were there any other body parts found. The police were called, and soon the media was in attendance.

Ohmer reported to the press with some authority that the foot could not have been in the stomach very long based on its condition. He further stated that it was obviously a fatal wound, and if she was alive when bitten, she had surely bled to death.

Although investigators checked with many municipalities along the shore, there were no recent reports of missing women. The individual was not

believed to be a swimmer, as she was wearing a shoe and stocking. Authorities hypothesized that she may have fallen off a boat or a dock, but since no one reported her missing, the case remains open.

The mystery endures, not what did the shark have for lunch, but who did it have for lunch?

AUGUST 27, 1913

LAVALLETTE, NJSAF #15

Although Captain John Steifbold and his son lived in Trenton during most of the year, they spent most of the summer in the small fishing village of Lavallette, New Jersey. Located on the Barnegat Peninsula, it had only a handful of year-round residents but boasted a population of a few hundred each summer.

In 1913, Lavallette had yet to gain popularity as a resort town. In addition to being difficult to reach, the amenities of running water, electricity and sewage disposal were not available on the peninsula. The accommodations were somewhat Spartan, but the Steifbolds didn't mind. They spent hours watching the working boats come and go at the docks and soon made friends with several fishermen who invited them to tag along on fishing trips.

They had only been in town less than a day when they met a fisherman they had befriended the previous summer. He invited them to accompany his crew on a run the next day to the fishing banks several miles off the coast.

Before dawn the next morning, the two were waiting for the captain at the dock. While the crew prepared for departure, the captain showed them the new ketch rigging that had recently been fitted and the narrow but deep well that was used to keep the catch alive until they returned to shore.

The deck of the smack was a beehive of activity, and within a few minutes, the captain had raised anchor and eased away from the dock. Once away from the shore, the sails were set, and the boat headed for the fishing banks.

They had barely arrived at their destination before the trawling net was released from the stern under the watchful eye of the first mate. The boat began a slow and methodical sweep of the sea bottom. After a while, a signal was given, and all hands hastened to the deck. Using a small cranking device and the muscle power of the crew, the great net was slowly lifted from the water.

The fishing fleet relied on the wind for power and the skills of the captain and crew to bring in a bountiful catch. *Historical postcard, authors' collection.*

As each batch of fish was brought up, crew members on each side began sorting the slippery, wiggling catch. The bycatch was tossed back into the sea, and the keepers went directly into the ship's well.

Suddenly, there were shouts as the crank grunted to a stop. Something was thrashing about near the stern. It was shaking the boat, making loud thumping noises and splashing water everywhere. One or two crew members took a step back, but another called out to the captain that they had caught a shark.

As the men attempted to untangle the net without getting bit or slammed by the huge tail, others ran to get weapons. The shark opened its giant mouth, exposing its jagged rows of spear-like teeth, and at the same time thrashed its great tail every which way, smashing against the side of the ship.

The crew gave the net one last big tug, bringing the shark closer to the stern. As soon as it was in range, they peppered it with harpoons, gaffs and boat hooks. In a few minutes, the shark lay motionless, looking much like a giant pincushion.

There was no way they could bring the immense fish on board. While two men tied the shark to the side of the vessel, the remainder of the crew hustled to bring in the remainder of the catch and secure the netting.

The smack sailed to the shore, where the twelve-foot-long carcass was gutted. But what they found startled even the most experienced fisherman. Among the stomach contents of the eight-hundred-pound shark were a twenty-pound turtle and part of a man's leg. The human limb, still wearing part of a trouser, sock and a man's shoe, had been

severed at the shin with the skill of a surgeon. A lengthy search for the remainder of the body proved fruitless, and not one local municipality reported anyone missing.

As is sometimes the case, there is not always a witness to record or publicize a shark attack. But in this instance, the evidence is obvious, the culprit is known; only the identity of the victim is unknown.

THE SUMMER OF 1916

1916

A SUMMER OF HORROR

CHAPTER 4

The summer of 1916 is best known as the summer of horror. While the resort hotels, boardwalks and beaches would flourish, they would also receive some unwanted guests in their waters: the well-known apex predator, the shark.

Despite rumors of war, people were generally optimistic until spring, when the cases of polio bloomed into an epidemic, killing and crippling thousands. More people than ever flocked to the Jersey shore to escape the heat of the city and the plague of illness. By mid-June, it felt more like the end of August. Local resorts were bustling, as the shore languished under an umbrella of heat and humidity

On June 30, 1916, everything changed; yet no one could foresee the horror that was about to spread northward from Atlantic City along the Jersey shore. Within a fortnight, local beaches would be terrorized by a wave of shark attacks, all of which made humans their prey. These are the accounts of that summer of horror here along the Jersey shore. They are New Jersey Shark Attack Files #16–22.

JUNE 30, 1916

ATLANTIC CITY, NJSAF #16

The summer of 1916 promised to be memorable on many accounts. The United States had managed to remain out of the war in Europe thus far, business was good and jobs were plentiful. President Wilson moved his summer White House to Long Branch. It was an era of newfound free time for workers, the papers were filled with the exploits of Boston's Babe Ruth and the price of the Model T had dropped to $500.

Seaside resorts were booming as more people than ever flocked to the Jersey shore. It was customary at that time for young men of all classes to take an ocean dip in the late afternoon before dinner. This is perhaps what brought the unnamed young man to the beach in North Atlantic City on June 30. Dressed in the customary black tank top and tight black shorts, he crossed the sand and made straight for the wading ropes along the side. He held on as he waded past the surf and then let go and moved toward the center of the beach.

He paused to watch several middle-aged fanny dunkers who stood in the surf and merely bent their knees so that an approaching wave splashed against their bottoms. Later he would say that something made him turn away from the humorous scene and look out over the ocean. That is when he saw a large dark fin cutting through the water heading straight for him.

He lurched toward the wading ropes and grabbed on. But when he glanced back, the fin was nearly upon him. A blood-curdling scream echoed across the water as the rope fell from his grasp. Something that felt like giant pliers were gripping his flesh. He screamed once more as he felt his flesh being ripped away. In an instant, there was only searing pain. Bystanders helped him to shore as a stream of blood marked their path. The flesh from his heel was stripped from his foot, and the gaping wound was bleeding profusely.

As there is no record that the attack was fatal, it is assumed the youth survived the attack, although we are uncertain of the extent of the damage to his foot or its effect on his mobility. For this young man, the summer did not begin so favorably, but he did survive to swim another day. This was the first attack of the summer of horror.

JULY 1, 1916

BEACH HAVEN, NJSAF #17

Just like many other summer mornings in Beach Haven, temperatures were in the eighties and the sun shone brightly on a beach town bustling with activity. Located just twenty miles north of Atlantic City, Beach Haven had become a popular tourist destination ever since the coming of the railroad in the 1870s.

On that Saturday, the express train from Camden arrived in Beach Haven at five o'clock, right on time. It was bursting with anxious and excited beachgoers. The exuberant crowd included a prominent Philadelphia physician, Eugene Vansant, along with his teenage daughters and his twenty-three-year-old son, Charles. Anxious to avoid the infantile paralysis epidemic ravaging the city, the doctor had booked rooms at the exclusive Engleside Hotel in Beach Haven for an entire week.

As soon as they were checked in, Charles lobbed his things into a cupboard and headed out for a swim, without waiting for his family to join him. He dashed out of the Engleside to the boardwalk bathhouses nearby, where he changed into swim attire before stepping out onto the warm sand. He was met by a warm sea breeze and a playful Chesapeake retriever that began to trail him along the surf.

Just as Charles entered the water, with the dog at his heels, he noticed his father and sister Louise standing near the lifeguard stand. He gave them a halfhearted wave and then plunged into the water. He swam past the lifelines and then to a point just beyond the breakers where the water was about chest high. Once again, he tried to entice the dog. Despite his callings and waving, the pup would not budge. The dog stared at him for a few minutes and then turned and made a hasty retreat to the beach.

Although it was well past five o'clock, the beach was crowded. Some were chatting with friends, reading the evening paper or surveying the bathers frolicking in the water. Several witnesses would later claim they had seen Charles calling out for the dog just as they noticed a large dark shadow moving beyond the breakers heading in his direction.

Suddenly, a loud, piercing scream echoed across the water. Charles was seen to suddenly propel himself toward shore. The second shriek resonated so loudly that it brought the beach crowd to their feet. Thrashing about wildly and screeching in pain, Charles was soon encircled in a pool of scarlet water.

The first scream had caught the attention of lifeguard Alexander Otto. He was racing toward Charles even before the second shrieks were heard. Clasping ahold of the flailing victim, Otto began towing him through the breakers toward shore. Even as they neared the beach, the long dark shadow continued to stalk its prey.

It wasn't until Otto had his victim in about eighteen inches of water that the shark broke away and disappeared into the depths. Onlookers hurried into the water to form a human chain to assist the lifeguard with the severely wounded man.

Charles's wounds were indeed horrifying. The flesh was ripped away from his hip to his upper left knee, revealing bloody, raw bone. His shredded right thigh spewed blood in an endless torrent, spilling across the sand and staining it a dark burgundy.

First aid was immediate. Dr. Vansant rushed to his son's side, as did another physician who was nearby. Charles was whisked to the hotel, where, despite further efforts, he hemorrhaged and was pronounced dead at 6:46 p.m. He had only been in Beach Haven for an hour and fifteen minutes, and now he was dead.

The shark was believed to be either a sand tiger or great white of about nine feet and weighing about five hundred pounds. While some maintained that it was totally dark in color, others said it had a whitish underbelly. For the Vansant family, it hardly mattered; their son was dead.

As we might imagine, the local shore communities were dismayed by the attack. Although it was the primary topic of conversation all along the Jersey shore, it didn't receive national media attention. The *New York Times* did publish an account of the attack but buried it on page eighteen. Averse to crediting it to a shark, the paper referred to it as an "assault by an unknown fish."

As horrific as the news was, locals knew that the economy of the area relied on the summer tourist industry. Many sought to identify the attack as an extraordinarily rare event. With the Fourth of July holiday just a few days away, resort and community leaders went one step further. They responded with protective measures as well as a major public relations campaign. Local communities followed the actions of the Engleside Hotel, which hastily installed metal netting about three hundred yards from shore to protect the beaches. Extra guards were placed both on the beaches and in small boats just beyond the breakers. Politicians, community leaders and experts rushed to reassure the public that the beaches were safe.

THE ENGLESIDE TENNIS CLUB COURTS, BEACH HAVEN, N. J.

Twenty-three-year-old Charles Vansant, a guest at the Engleside Hotel, was the second victim of the shark attacks of 1916. *Courtesy of the New York Public Library.*

Meanwhile, the Vansant family planned the funeral for their only son. Although the resort owners held their breath for a successful Fourth of July, the respite would not last long. This was the summer of 1916, July 6 was just five days away and just a few miles north, the Spring Lake beaches were open.

JULY 6, 1916

SPRING LAKE, NJSAF #18

Spring Lake, a quiet, upscale enclave, is a picturesque and friendly beach town known as the Jewel of the Jersey Shore. A small business district features trendy shops, cafés and classic architecture. It is surrounded by tree-lined streets and carefully manicured lawns that complement the mostly classic and palatial residences.

Even one hundred years ago, the town was a seaside resort catering to the ultra-elite of society. Among the luxurious hotels was the famous oceanfront Essex and Sussex, celebrated for its unparalleled accommodations and services.

Still a landmark today, the Essex and Sussex is the site of the third shark attack of 1916 where Swiss-born George Bruder lost his life. *Authors' photo.*

It was not surprising that as the polio outbreak worsened during the early summer of 1916, the requests for hotel reservations swelled in Spring Lake. Even high society fled the epidemic. Some of the visitors may have known of the shark attack in Beach Haven a few days prior, but the newspapers had not covered the incident in detail. The local resorts certainly did not publicize the event. It was business as usual in Spring Lake—or so it seemed.

There was, however, a quiet apprehension among the business community. Lifeguards were instructed to look for triangle-shaped fins and dark shadows in the water and admonished to be extra diligent in their scrutiny of the beaches.

The Independence Day holiday was like any other in Spring Lake. The summer "cottages" were all occupied, and the hotels were teeming with guests. The Essex and Sussex was particularly resplendent this holiday, hosting multiple soirees and high-society events. These included a spectacular formal dinner party attended by numerous government officials, cabinet members and leaders of industry and commerce. Unknown to all, one of

the servers at the event that night, Charles Bruder, would soon become a name known to one and all.

On Thursday, July 6, Spring Lake was bustling. Many guests stayed on for the remainder of the week after the Fourth of July festivities. By nine o'clock that morning, the shore was lumbering under excessive heat and humidity. At the Essex and Sussex, guests sought the cooling breezes from the wide verandas as staff scurried about meeting every request and petition from the demanding clientele.

Charles Bruder, a twenty-eight-year-old Swiss national, was spending his third summer here at the Essex and Sussex. He was captain of the bellhops, as well as part-time waiter and assistant to the concierge. He spent the morning toting bags, trays and parcels. He delivered messages, ran errands and assisted in any way possible to ensure that the hotel guests were happy. Bruder, well-spoken and polite, did his job with finesse and grace and was very popular with both staff and guests.

The day was intolerably hot, and there was no relief in sight as noon approached. Bruder had very few days off recently. Yet it was nearly 1:45 p.m. before he and his friend Henry Nolan, the elevator operator, could take their much-needed lunch break. Like many other employees, Bruder often took advantage of this break for a cooling dip in the ocean. Today was no exception.

The moment they were free, they hurried from the hotel and dashed along the boardwalk to the employee bathhouse and beach at the South Pavilion. Dressed in simple black swimwear, the two darted from the bathhouse and sprinted into the water, swimming beyond the mass of bathers just beyond the breakers. Bruder, however, was a strong swimmer and swam away from his friend until he was about 130 yards offshore. It had been unbearably hot in the hotel all morning, and Bruder was relishing every moment of his midday dip.

Just then, a scream of agony resounded across the water, and a woman rushed the lifeguard stand screaming that a red canoe had upset beyond the breakers. At that moment, the two guards spotted a lone swimmer thrashing about wildly in a circle of red water. Bolting from the stand, they raced to the boat, shoved it into the surf and began to row with all their might toward the flailing victim.

They knew at once what had happened. As the boat entered the mass of red water, one guard caught a glimpse of a dark form streaking toward them. Bruder lurched upward for a moment before falling back into the water. They extended an oar to him, but he was unable to hold on. As

the shark charged once more Bruder was yanked over the gunwale into the boat.

"A shark bit off my legs," he muttered, before falling into unconsciousness. He lay limp and motionless as blood gushed from his wounds, forming large pools of scarlet that ran along the length of the boat. The two experienced guards frowned and exchanged knowing glances. The young Swiss man died before reaching the shore.

The catastrophic injuries became apparent to all as Bruder's lifeless body was brought ashore and laid gently on the beach. His right leg was totally severed halfway between the ankle and the knee, leaving jagged shreds of flesh hanging from the wound. His left foot was totally missing, and both the tibia and fibula were severed just below the knee. A circular gash above the right knee revealed torn and jagged skin and muscle. On the right side of his abdomen, a rounded gouge penetrated deep into the abdominal cavity.

Although the house physicians from the New Monmouth Hotel rushed to assist, there was nothing they could do. Charles Bruder was dead. The doctors spent most of their time dealing with hysterical beachgoers who fainted from the sight of the horrific attack. Hotel employees rushed to the beach to assist numerous guests so traumatized by the sight of the mutilated body that they required assistance getting back to their rooms.

The response up and down the shore was immediate. Within minutes, beaches all along the coast were emptied. At the Essex and Sussex, there were abrupt cancellations, numerous distraught guests seeking reassurance and a staff overwhelmed by both the death of their friend and the additional demands put on them by the hotel guests.

With six more weeks of the tourist season remaining, resort owners and community leaders sprang into action. Any beach without protective metal nettings had them hastily installed. Nearly every town hired patrols of small boats not only to guard the beaches but also to eliminate any sharks sighted in local waters.

A few local papers took to print with sensational accounts of the attack. The *Belmar Advisor* warned the locals of "man-eaters" in our waters. On the other hand, the *Asbury Park Press* sought to assuage the fears of its readers. Its coverage featured the extensive emergency procedures taken to ensure the safety of both citizens and visitors.

This time, the attack made national news. Papers in Boston, Chicago, San Francisco and Washington carried the news on their front pages. The *New York Times* carried the story as its headline the following morning.

Within days, a contentious press conference of three experts from the American Museum of Natural History was held to clarify their recent publication, which indicated that sharks were harmless sea creatures. When pressed by reporters, the trio held that the netting being installed on local beaches would ensure the safety of the public.

By July 10, the attacks were off the front page, and local businesses began to pick up the pieces and salvage what they could of the summer season. There was little talk of sharks, for they were praying that it was all over.

Little did the Jersey shore know that there was more terror to come. Two days later, just thirty miles up the coast, the small working-class town of Matawan would experience a series of shark attacks unlike any other.

JULY 12, 1916

MATAWAN, NJSAF #19-22

Four of the shark attacks during that summer of 1916 occurred on one day and in one locality. These attacks are presented as a unit as the events of that horrific day are intertwined with one another, resulting in a day of true terror in one small New Jersey town.

Wednesday, July 12, 1916, began like any other summer day in Matawan, New Jersey. But by the time the day had ended, it would prove to be unlike any day the residents had ever known and one they would never forget. Within the space of a few hours, the community would be thrust into the national spotlight as four shark attacks, occurring within a few minutes of one another, would claim the lives of two local citizens and injure two others. As Matawan is an inland community, the attacks came totally unexpected, despite the recent attacks farther south in resort areas along the ocean.

Located thirty miles north of Spring Lake, situated on a bluff fifty feet above the creek that bears its name, is Matawan, New Jersey. Despite their proximity and the fact that both towns are located within the county of Monmouth, Matawan was, in many respects, worlds away from the posh resort setting of Spring Lake. The blue-collar population of Matawan, some twelve hundred strong, worked mostly in the maritime industrial factories and businesses that dotted Matawan Creek. By 1916, Matawan was home to numerous businesses, which included a clay and brick plant, a title firm, a bag company, a gristmill and a basket factory. The flourishing business

district on Main Street featured an array of shops, including dry goods and variety stores, a hardware, a barber, a tailor and a bakery.

Nearby Matawan Creek, which locals referred to as the "crick," is a tidal estuary that snakes its way through eleven miles of marshes and lowlands until it reaches Raritan Bay. The once busy docks that carried local products to the coast had silted by 1916 and were largely abandoned. Now the creek served as a popular spot for fishing and crabbing and, during the summer months, as the neighborhood swimming hole for local kids.

Like other towns across New Jersey that summer of 1916, the conversations on the streets and in the cafés were of the war in Europe, the polio epidemic and most recently of the shark attacks farther down the shore in Beach Haven and Spring Lake. Fear of local shark attacks was not on anyone's mind that summer, as Matawan lies eleven miles inland at the end of the shallow, somewhat brackish estuary.

The timeline of events begins as the day breaks on the sleeping village of Matawan. Locals headed off to work to face another hot and humid day. The following shark attacks all occurred that day, July 12, within the span of about an hour and a half. The events of that day are presented chronologically to put the day of horror into perspective.

The air felt heavy and fetid even at sunrise in Matawan that morning. Families awoke early and began their chores. Many had risen earlier than usual hoping to complete the day's tasks before the temperatures reached their climax. Indeed, the thermometers would top off at ninety-six degrees later that day.

The Stillwell family was already rousted from their beds even as the sun was rising. By 6:00 a.m., William Stillwell and his eleven-year-old son, Lester, were eating a hearty breakfast of ham, eggs and fresh bread with jam. Mrs. Stillwell was packing cold sandwiches and small cakes into metal lunch pails for their noon meal. She looked over at the table where the two were chewing on the last of their bread and jam and smiled. She was pleased to see her son and husband laughing and talking together.

Lester was an epileptic, so it gave her peace of mind knowing that they were spending most of the day together. Although Lester's seizures were infrequent, his father would know what to do in case of an attack. Lester, who was anxiously awaiting his twelfth birthday the next week, worked that summer as an apprentice with his father at the Anderson Basket Factory. The Stillwells believed it was good for a boy to learn a trade when he was young, as it would serve him well someday. Besides, Lester was proud to contribute to the family income with his job nailing together peach baskets.

At 6:30 a.m., the two gave her a quick hug and kiss and headed out the kitchen door and walked along the main road in town on their way to the factory on Water Street. Along the way, they passed friends and neighbors who were also on their way to work at local mills, factories or warehouses.

Like many other shopkeepers, twenty-four-year-old Stanley Fisher had arrived early to open his tailoring and dry-cleaning shop. Once the windows were pulled back to allow the morning breeze to enter, he set about preparing the shop for business. Stanley tidied his store and then double-checked the front window display, which he used to showcase his tailoring skills.

Next door, Arthur Smith, a local carpenter, was stacking lumber and tools against the building. He had shouted a greeting to Stanley upon arrival as he set to work repairing the facing of the storefront. He, too, had started his work early, hoping to be finished before the heat of the day.

About the same time, Thomas Cottrell, a well-known retired boat captain, headed out for his usual morning stroll, which was more of a meandering, along the creek-side docks and fishing haunts.

Lester and his father, meanwhile, hurried into the factory and began their jobs in earnest. As his dad's apprentice, Lester's job was to nail together peach baskets. The minute he arrived, he grabbed the first basket and set to work. His father was pleased that Lester had such a strong work ethic. He told his son that if he worked hard that morning, he could leave work early and spend the afternoon swimming in the creek with his friends. That was all Lester needed to hear. He bent over his workstation, never looking up, nailing peach basket after peach basket as carefully but as quickly as he could.

About the time Lester started work, another young man, fourteen-year-old Joseph Dunn of New York City, was leaving his home on 178th Street en route to the train station. Along with his brother Michael, he was bound for a one-day visit to see his aunt in Cliffwood Beach, New Jersey. The duo was excited to escape the heat of the city and have a "day in paradise," as Joseph called his shore visit. They would spend the day swimming and playing baseball.

At one o'clock, Lester and his father paused for lunch. There was not even the slightest breeze in the factory to provide cooling that Wednesday. They sat quietly eating their sandwiches. Several of Lester's pals came by to find out if he would be coming down to swim. His father looked at the basket count. Lester had finished 150 baskets that morning. His dad looked at the boy sweating through his thin shirt and smiled. "That's a good job today, son," he said. "You can go to the crick at a quarter of two."

It was also about one o'clock when Thomas Cottrell, the retired captain, began to saunter back toward town. He had just reached the trolley drawbridge when he noticed several Stormy Petrels on the railing. He had never seen the offshore birds so far inland. He paused to study the unusual visitors when his gaze fell on the surface of the water below. A raspy gasp escaped his throat. He refocused his eyes on the sight below. It couldn't be, but it was. An enormous dark form was moving westward with the tide toward the old Matawan docks. The silhouette was obvious to any mariner: it was a shark.

Cottrell rushed to the bridge keeper's booth to phone John Mulsoff, the town marshal. When Mulsoff, who was also the town barber, answered the call, the entire conversation could be heard throughout the small barbershop. Cottrell was considered by many as a bit of a character who was well known for spinning countless yarns from his fishing days. He told Cottrell that there was nothing to worry about and reminded him that sharks don't swim in brackish water like Matawan Creek. The constable chuckled, saying that Cottrell had just read too many newspaper accounts of the shark attacks down in Spring Lake.

Cottrell, however, was certain of what he had seen. He also knew that the local kids used the creek as a swimming hole most afternoons. He jumped into his small motorboat and headed upstream to warn others. He looked at his watch; it was 1:45 p.m.

As Cottrell headed upstream, Lester was excused from work. He joined his friends who had waited for him at the factory. They bolted down the street heading for the Wykoff dock, peeling off clothes as they went. Just then, Cottrell passed the dock, but the trees and shrubs lining the creek blocked his view. They didn't see one another.

By 1:50 p.m., clothes were slung on nearby bushes and the group plunged into the muddy brown creek. Although it was more like a cool brown gravy, the boys didn't mind. Despite its appearance, the water was wonderfully refreshing. By this time, Cottrell was running down Main Street warning anyone he encountered of the shark swimming up the creek. Most people dismissed the warning; no one had ever heard of a shark swimming eleven miles inland.

Back at the Wykoff pier, there was some friendly splashing and a few competitive barbs. The boys began demonstrating their abilities at floating atop the murky surface. Not to be outdone, Lester joined in the fun. He pushed himself onto his back and spread out his arms as he shouted, "Watch me float!"

Just then Lester's pal Ally O'Hara felt something rough, like sandpaper, brush against his leg. He looked at the water but saw only a dark shadow. Out of the corner of his eye, he saw what looked like an old plank floating toward Lester.

Before he could call out, the dark form rammed into his friend, heaving his small body upward. Lester's eyes were wild and unknowing as he fell back into the muddy creek. Frozen in horror, the boys watched the attack in silence. As the large dorsal fin pierced the surface of the water, the huge black form latched onto Lester once more. It lurched slightly, exposing its white underbelly and huge gleaming teeth. There was a scream of sorts and a gurgle as Lester vanished beneath the blood-tainted water of Matawan Creek.

The boys scrambled from the water without stopping to put on a stitch of clothes. They ran until they reached Main Street, screeching, "A shark got Lester!" It was just 2:10 p.m. when they burst into Stanley Fisher's tailor shop. The twenty-four-year-old tailor, who frequently played baseball with the boys, dropped his scissors. He knew that Lester was epileptic and assumed the boy had a seizure. As he rushed out the door, he shouted for help to Arthur Smith, the carpenter working next door. He, too, dropped his tools and joined in the mad dash to the creek. As they passed Red Burlew on Water Street, Stanley repeated his call for help. The three men sprinted to the edge of the creek, searching the surface for the boy. Seeing nothing, they hopped into a nearby boat and rowed across the swimming hole, scouring the surface. There was no sight of Lester.

Although they saw blood in the murky water, Stanley thought that the boy must have hit his head on a rock when he fell from the seizure. Precious time was passing. The trio returned to shore, stripped to their underwear and plunged into the water. Again and again, they dove into the muddy creek, frantically searching for the missing boy.

A crowd had gathered along the banks, including Lester Stillwell's mother and father. After about thirty minutes, the would-be rescuers realized that the boy must surely have drowned. They continued to dive, hoping to at least recover the body for the heartbroken parents.

They saw nothing in the murky creek except a few faint currents of red emanating from the bottom. Suddenly, carpenter Arthur Smith rushed to the surface, grimacing in pain. He had been whacked by something that felt like coarse sandpaper. Blood was oozing from his leg as he swam for shore. He would learn later that he had been the second victim of a shark that day. Stanley and Red watched as Arthur was pulled onto the creek bank.

They knew their search was futile. But once again they saw Lester's mother weeping uncontrollably. They took deep breaths and plunged once more into the creek.

Stanley spotted the boy's body along the bottom. He grabbed a leg and tried to surface. When the body would not budge, he gave it one more tug and headed upward. As he broke the surface of the water, the crowd gasped. At that very same moment, Stanley Fisher shrieked, "Oh, my God!"

The great beast had latched onto Stanley's thigh. Witnesses report that he fought the shark with all his might amid the red soapsuds that encircled him. In one last effort, he struggled to swim toward shore, shouting, "He got me, the shark got me!"

A few yards away, two other rescuers who had manned a rowboat in search of the child saw the battle and rushed to Stanley's aid. They began beating on the shark's head with their oars until it released Stanley from its grasp. They yanked the wounded tailor into their boat, where the severity of his injuries became immediately apparent.

By 2:30 p.m., Stanley Fisher was lying on the bank of the creek. Dr. Reynolds, the first physician to arrive, tried to stop the blood that was gushing from the young man's body. Stanley remained conscious for some time, frequently asking how bad the wound appeared.

The would-be rescuer's wounds were severe. A wide laceration on his right thigh ran from his hip to his knee. At least ten pounds of flesh were removed, leaving the remainder of his leg a bloody mass of raked and ragged flesh.

It was obvious that Stanley required immediate surgery to save his life. The only option for such intensive care was Monmouth Memorial Hospital, twenty miles away in Long Branch. Dr. Reynolds believed that Fisher would not withstand transport by automobile. Yet the train to Long Branch would not arrive for another two hours.

As the physician fought to save Stanley Fisher's life, the Dunn brothers and their pals were enjoying the cool, if muddy, waters of the creek four hundred yards downstream. Suddenly, they heard a great commotion in the distance and then the distinct shouts of "Shark!"

The boys raced toward the creek bank. All the others had climbed onto the dock and were watching as Joseph Dunn, last in line, stepped up onto the old wooden ladder. Something grabbed his leg, yanking him back into the creek. Joseph screamed in agony. He thrashed about, crying, "My leg, my leg!"

With only Joseph's head above the water and the circle of red blood surrounding him growing wider, the other boys tried to form a human chain to pull him ashore. But it was his brother Michael who dove into the water

and tugged on Joseph, trying to pull him from the clutches of the shark. Jacob Lefferts, who was fishing nearby, heard their shouts and rushed to the creek. Fully clothed, he dove into the creek to help Michael free his brother.

In these few minutes, Cottrell had sped down the creek and reached the scene. At 2:45 p.m., he loaded Joseph in his boat and rushed him back to the Wykoff dock for medical treatment. The shark attacks in Matawan Creek ceased. But the crisis was far from over.

Joseph Dunn was brought to the Wykoff dock, where Dr. Colley, another local physician, had just arrived. Joseph was not bleeding as severely as Fisher, although his injuries were serious. When a local man who owned a 1913 Buick offered to drive the doctor and Joseph to St. Peters Hospital in New Brunswick, the doctor agreed. The trio immediately set out on the sixteen-mile trip up the winding road that led to New Brunswick. Although there were no crushed bones or lacerated arteries, Joseph's left leg was cut to ribbons from the knee to the ankle. He would spend the next fifty-nine days recuperating in the hospital.

Meanwhile, Stanley Fisher lay bleeding in Matawan waiting for the train. Dr. Reynolds attempted to comfort the stricken man as much as he could. During the long hours of waiting, Stanley reportedly spoke of the attack as he drifted in and out of consciousness. At 5:06 p.m., he was put on the train, which sped nonstop to Long Branch. He was awake as he was taken into the operating room, where he continued to mumble about the attack as he faded into unconsciousness. Before he passed away, he clearly stated, "I did my duty." Stanley Fisher, the third victim of the shark attacks that day, died at 6:45 p.m.

Matawan could not have been more shocked if a bomb had gone off on Main Street. In a small town where everyone knows everyone else, such savage attacks and loss of life are unfathomable. In the ensuing hours, the town both mourned and sought revenge for the unforgivable attacks. One child was dead, another injured. One good Samaritan rescuer had lost his life, and another lay scared and bedridden with over a dozen stitches.

Within hours, the mayor would offer a reward for the killing of the shark responsible for the carnage in Matawan. But it was the townsfolk who took the revenge into their own hands. Men arrived creek side bearing shotguns, harpoons, rakes, spears, clubs and even axes. More than fifteen capture nets were strung across the creek, and before nightfall, the call went out to the hardware store for dynamite. Determined that the killer would not escape, the dynamiting of Matawan Creek began in earnest at dark and continued well into the night.

The good folks of Matawan gather creek side as rescuers search for the child's body. *Courtesy of Mark Sceurman,* Weird New Jersey Magazine.

Immediately, the national media descended on the small town. The next morning, Thursday, July 13, the *Matawan Tribune* headline read "Man Eating Shark Causes Death of Man and Boy." The frenzied hunt continued, with many killing anything they happened to see in the nearby waters. Finally, as darkness fell, a heavy thunderstorm that evening chased nearly everyone into their homes.

On Friday, July 14, Lester's Stillwell's body was recovered when it floated to the surface about 150 yards from the attack. His left ankle was chewed off, his left thigh mangled from hip to knee. His left abdomen was ruptured, the intestines pulled out and herniated. Both his right hip and chest muscles were shredded and eaten away. As if that was not enough, large chunks of flesh had been torn from his little body.

Saturday, July 16, was a day of mourning in Matawan as both of the victims were laid to rest in Rosewood Cemetery. Families would grieve for years; a town would struggle for understanding and a nation would face the summer with bated breath.

Although the day of carnage may have ended, the uproar caused by the attacks was just beginning. The small town was overwhelmed by the influx of humanity. There were the crowds of the well-intended, the sightseers and the morbidly curious. Most of all there was the media, present in mass. They were everywhere, searching for a lead, begging for interviews, pursuing yet another angle to the story. Countless headlines, one more sensational than

the last, were published without verification of their validity. So many false reports arose that people didn't know what to believe. All of this must have leached the strength from the good folks of Matawan.

Over one hundred years have passed, and many of the questions about the Matawan attacks remain unanswered, or at least controversial. It is not possible to authoritatively identify the species of shark responsible for these attacks. Some claim it was a young great white shark, while others declare it was a sand tiger or bull shark.

It is reasonable to assume that since all four attacks occurred within a few minutes of one another, a single shark did the damage in Matawan Creek. But it is unlikely we will ever know if the culprit paid for his deeds with his life. We know that the creek was dynamited mercilessly that night and that for days countless hunters took to their boats to hunt down and slaughter anything that resembled a large fish anywhere near the vicinity.

Local newspapers from the time reported several accounts of large sharks being caught in the area. This includes the well-known account of July 14, when New Yorker Michael Schleisser, a taxidermist and animal trainer for Barnum and Bailey, caught an eight-and-a-half-foot, 325-pound white shark in Raritan Bay. According to press accounts, the abdomen contained 15 pounds of human flesh. Also found was an eleven-inch piece of shin bone, most likely that of a youngster. Others dispute the identification of the shin bone, insisting it was a partial piece and therefore belonged to a grown man.

Several other claims include one from Captain Cottrell. Three days after the attacks, he declared he had caught a 230-pound, seven-foot bull shark at the mouth of Matawan Creek. This capture was questioned, however, when a worker at a fishery in Monmouth Beach testified that he had sold Cottrell a shark for five dollars. He further said that Cottrell asserted he was going to put the beast on display and charge ten cents. Cottrell was true to his word. He packed the shark in ice and did indeed set up his "man-eater" exhibit at the Keyport Bridge Fishery, where he drew huge crowds for several days.

It should be noted that on July 13, just one day after the Matawan attacks, there were two shark events reported in nearby Sheepshead Bay, Brooklyn, just twelve miles from Matawan Creek. Gertrude Hoffman reported seeing a dorsal fin speeding toward her during her morning swim in the bay. She began beating furiously on the water, scaring away the beast. Thomas Richards was also swimming in the bay when shouts of "shark!" by an alert companion enabled him to make it safely back to his boat, suffering only a minor abrasion to his ankle.

One hundred years after the attack, Matawan paid tribute to the lost child and the hero tailor who lost his life trying to rescue him. The memorial dedicated on July 12, 2016, marks the site of the attack. *Authors' photo.*

The discussion of the Matawan shark attacks is not likely to end anytime soon. There are dozens of theories and equal numbers of devotees supporting their individual hypotheses. We may not know for certain how many sharks were involved, nor which species was responsible. But we do know of the lives damaged or lost and of the tragedy and heroism in the small New Jersey town named Matawan.

JULY 13, 1916

SEA BRIGHT, NJSAF #58

The Sea Bright fishing fleet headed out as usual during the pre-dawn hours of July 13, 1916. Although nearby Matawan was still reeling from the horror of the previous day, details of the event remained sketchy, and local fishermen were at sea long before the daily paper arrived.

George White and his two-man crew were fishing just off Sea Bright. Expecting another hot day, they hoped to fill their keeper and return to shore before the heat set in. They had just spotted a huge gray shark circling their small craft when it suddenly rammed them full force. The impact capsized the boat and tossed the men into the water.

With no other craft near enough to hear their cries, the three latched onto the side of the overturned hull and began shouting and pounding

the surface with their legs. Each time they paused to rest, the great shark began inching its way toward them once more. Although churning waters seemed to hold the beast at bay, the trio realized they could not continue this much longer.

George ordered the two men to try to upright the boat while he floated near the bow, kicking his legs with all his might, creating a great thrashing and splashing of water. The two fishermen managed to rotate the craft just enough so that it turned upright. One by one, they scampered on board and then yanked George over the gunwale into the bottom of the boat. They hauled in their net and made for shore.

When they arrived on shore, they shared their adventures with Captain Lockwood, who not only told them of the gruesome attacks in Matawan the previous day but also inspected their hull and found the telltale tooth embedded in the wood bottom. All three were uninjured and felt fortunate they had suffered only the loss of a day's pay.

1917–1926

SEPTEMBER 21, 1917

SEA BRIGHT, NJSAF #23

Despite the warm weather, sunny skies and wide clean beaches, the summer season at the Jersey shore in 1917 was lackluster at best. The April declaration that brought the United States into World War I had curtailed the summer's festivities and dampened people's spirits. The almost immediate implementation of conscription hung over the heads of the young men, leaving everyone feeling a bit vulnerable.

In mid-September, a team of lifeguards in Sea Bright stood watch over a nearly abandoned beach, although a few people sauntered along the surf. Sometimes they stopped to pick up shells or pieces of sea glass, but most had the war on their minds and simply stood and looked out to sea. There had been no bathers all morning, no one used the rope lifeline that extended outward from the beach and no one called for assistance.

Daniel Thompson and his team members Arthur Johnson and Edmund Cline had guarded the beach for several years. They worked well together, helped one another as needed and took pride that their beach was always safe and clean.

Today, their conversation was about the war. Would they be called up for the military, how long would the war last and would the fighting spread to our shores? Daniel interrupted the glum discussion when he spied a brown

Spotting a fin is often the first and only indication that a shark is nearby. *Courtesy of www.pixababy.com.*

cask-shaped object bobbing in the water just beyond the breakers. After watching it for a few minutes, the team decided that they needed to tow the object off the breakers and away from their beach.

The three lifeguards gathered their rescue boards and some lengths of rope and headed into the ocean. They intended to tow the barrel farther out, where the current would catch it and take it away. When they reached the old wooden cask, they determined that it was empty. Resting on their floating boards, the trio began tying onto the barrel with the lengths of rope.

It was then that they spotted the shark. It was swimming very close to the breakers, between themselves and the beach. When the shark turned and moved in their direction, they dropped the ropes and sprang onto the rescue boards. Just then, a wave broke at their backs, and two of the guards rode the wave to shore. But Daniel was not quick enough; he missed the wave, and the shark sideswiped him. An intense burning spread the length of his leg, and as he reached for his board, it flipped away. Without hesitating, he threw his body onto the next wave and let it carry him closer to the shore. Once in shallow water, he staggered toward the beach.

When his friends reached Daniel, he had an open laceration on his knee. Otherwise, he was unhurt. They brought their colleague to shore and administered first aid. In a few days, a doctor declared that Daniel could return to work.

The team worked together that year until the beaches closed for the season. It would be the last time they ever worked together. By the next summer, they were all in the trenches of Europe.

JANUARY 1, 1923

OCEAN CITY, NJSAF #24–25

Despite Prohibition, New Year's was celebrated by millions of Americans with festive parties and holiday dinners in 1923. But for the fishermen of the Jersey shore, January 1 was just another workday. Like every other day, they got up in the middle of the night and were at sea when the sun rose. Holidays were few and far between for the fishermen of the fleet; they were family men with bills to pay and mouths to feed.

Although they had dressed for the frigid temperatures, the crew had to keep moving to keep from getting cold. The wind was biting, and it wasn't long before even hands wrapped in thick work gloves were numb. The trawler was fighting a choppy sea as it began the backbreaking work of bringing in the nets. The spray turned to icicles that hung from the men's hair and formed a solid layer on their coats and boots. Everyone was working quickly to get the nets in and the catch sorted and stowed. The faster they worked, the sooner they would be heading to shore and the warmth of the local pub.

They only had one more section of the net to bring aboard when, suddenly, the gears of the wench grunted to a stop. Something began to thrash about violently, spanking the stern of the boat. Before anyone could react, the entire net came crashing down, spilling hundreds of silvery flopping fish across the deck.

Still ensnared in the net was one very large and angry shark. The crew bolted as the creature flailed about, wriggling this way and that. The beast propelled itself from side to side, all the while flashing its huge teeth, snapping at anything that was near. Meanwhile, its giant tail slammed first one way and then another, sending much of the catch flying back into the sea.

Sharks are frequently bycatch for commercial netters and can be costly when nets are damaged or destroyed. *Courtesy NOAA Central Library of Historical Fisheries, Millard Freeman Officers and Crew.*

Some crew ran for weapons, while others fashioned ropes into lassos. One man attempted to tether the tail, but the animal swung its great appendage down on the man's thigh, breaking his leg instantly. Others trying to bind the snapping jaws of the beast suffered cuts and abrasions for their efforts.

Eventually, the beast was restrained and quickly dispatched by the crew. The wounded had their injuries attended to, and the corpse was tossed overboard. As is often the case, there was never an official report of the incident, so the total number of injuries is unclear. We do know that the shark perished and several members of the crew had both injuries and true shark tales to share that night at the pub.

Note that the Global Shark Attack File (GSAF) assigned two case numbers to this event but did not cite the reason. Currently, the NJSAF (New Jersey Shark Attack File) recognizes these two numbers until the investigation clears up the matter.

SPRING 1923

SEA BRIGHT, NJSAF #26

Richard Rodney lived in a little cottage in the old section of the barrier beach known as Galilee. He was known for being an avid fisherman; in fact, it was said that Richard would fish for anything that could swim. He could be found all along the coast and up and down the local estuaries doing one form of fishing or another. He was so often seen fishing in local waters that people wondered out loud if he ever worked at all.

Earlier that spring, Richard bought a used twenty-four-foot boat from an old fishing buddy that he named *Myria*. After that, he was nearly always seen in his boat just off the coast of Sea Bright. At first, he stayed very close to the shore, but as time went by, he became braver and began taking his boat farther out away from the beach. He spent hours aboard the *Myria*. He never complained about fishing; he was as happy catching a mossbunker as he was a striped bass. Richard truly loved to fish.

It is difficult to pinpoint the day Richard encountered the shark. We know it was 1923, and it is believed to have been sometime in early spring. The day was slightly overcast, although the temperatures were above average. The waters were calm as Richard piloted the boat around the tip of Sandy Hook and traveled a short distance south until he was just off the beach at Sea Bright. He was farther offshore than usual that day, but he could still see the outlines of the roofs back on shore.

He dropped anchor and was gathering his tackle when he noticed a large fin advancing through the water toward him. At first, the intruder circled the *Myria* and then disappeared into the depths. Then it surfaced once more and, without warning, burst through the water straight at him. The shark struck the boat along the side, just below the waterline, with its great head, shoving the small craft sideways. His tackle clattered as it slid across the deck, knocking over his thermos and lunch box.

Richard scanned the nearby water, but the shark was gone. Before he could sigh in relief, it returned and slammed against the boat once more. The sound of splintering wood made the hair stand up on the back of his neck. He rushed to raise the anchor and made for shore as quickly as he could. For a while, he was certain the shark was trailing him, but after a bit, it seemed to lose interest and cut off the chase.

After returning to the dock, he inspected his boat. Along the starboard side, just below the waterline, he found a single shark's tooth embedded in the hull. Richard never lost his love for fishing, although he seldom strayed from the local shore waters.

JULY 12, 1926

SEA BRIGHT, NJSAF #27

The second weekend of July 1926 was one of the busiest and warmest of the summer season. Visitors from across the region flocked to the shore

for the cooling ocean breezes, while both commercial and recreational fishermen took to the offshore waters with buckets of live bait and dreams of a spectacular catch. Andrew Peterson and Peter Jergerson, two local men, were no exception

The two had grown up along the shore and were inseparable as boys. They could always be found fishing or hunting for clams in local waters. About the time they got their first jobs as deckhands, the war came, and they were quickly conscripted into the service. Although the military didn't fit into their plans at the time, they managed to finagle assignments in the U.S. Navy.

When the war ended, they returned home. It was as if they had never been apart. They got good jobs with the new power company that was electrifying the local communities up and down the coast of New Jersey.

It wasn't long before they had scraped up enough money to buy an old weatherworn fishing boat, which they named the *Mary Sue*. Although it wasn't the best-looking vessel at the dock, it was seaworthy and came at the right price. They didn't have either the time or money to have the boat repainted before the summer season, but they took the *Mary Sue* fishing nearly every weekend. At first, they were cautious and fished only in Raritan Bay. But it wasn't long before they were heading offshore to the fishing banks some twenty miles off Sea Bright.

That day, July 12, 1926, was to be a day much like every other that summer. They arrived at the dock before dawn toting their boat poles, their food hamper, a water jug and thermos bottles of hot coffee. It wasn't long before Andrew cast off the lines, and Peter began to ease away from the dock and move into the inlet. They made steady progress and within a few minutes were in the bay heading for the tip of Sandy Hook. Peter set his compass, and they made their way southeast, moving away from the Sea Bright shore.

The waters were calm and the seas about as smooth as they get in the Atlantic. They soon arrived at the fishing banks, where they dropped anchor. Each man set about checking his lines and baiting his hooks. They cast from opposite sides of the boat before securing the rods. The two then settled down to wait for the first bite.

Andrew saw the fin first as it glided by the port side of the boat. It was distinctive, and he knew at once that it was a shark. The two began to follow the shark's movements as it began a wide circle around their boat. The first circular route of the great fish didn't concern them, but they exchanged furtive glances when the long dark creature made a second identical loop.

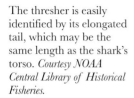

The thresher is easily identified by its elongated tail, which may be the same length as the shark's torso. *Courtesy NOAA Central Library of Historical Fisheries.*

On the third pass, the shark was close enough that Andrew could distinguish the telltale elongated caudal fin of the thresher shark. The creature was also distinctive due to its short snout and white underbelly.

Fishermen are never indifferent to a shark sighting, but they had no fear of the giant creature that seemed to be visiting them. They knew the thresher was considered a timid and solitary creature that usually preferred warmer and deeper waters.

When the shark began making ever-smaller circles around their boat, they rushed to their rods and began reeling in their lines as quickly as they could. There was no need to lose a good rig to a curious shark, for they assumed the creature would soon lose interest. But then the shark made yet another pass, drawing it even closer to the boat. The men laughed about the peculiar and sudden boldness of their visitor. Then, with a sudden burst of speed, the shark began yet another loop, only to break off and charge straight for the *Mary Sue*. It made a quick dive and at the very last minute slapped the hull with its gigantic tail. The boat shuddered and lurched sideways.

Before they could react, the thresher appeared once again and made a direct hit on the side of the boat. This time there was the distinct sound of splintering wood. The food hamper flew open, spilling its contents onto the deck. In the same instant, the bait bucket toppled over, mixing its contents with their sandwiches, and the thermos jugs rolled back and forth along the deck, ricocheting off the stern.

Peter raced to raise the anchor as Andrew maneuvered the boat away from the shark with as much speed as he could muster. As they hurried back to shore, Peter kept an eye out for any sign of water seeping into the boat.

They returned to shore unharmed, although empty handed, having caught not even one fish. And although the bait bucket upset, drenching their sandwiches, they suffered only a cracked thermos and the loss of the baitfish. The *Mary Sue* was unscathed, and both the fishermen and the thresher lived to perhaps meet yet another day.

AUGUST 24, 1926

SEASIDE PARK, NJSAF #28

Tuesday, August 24, 1926, started out like any other summer day at the Jersey shore during the 1920s. Known as the place for "family fun," Seaside was popular with families from the entire tristate region. They flocked in droves to the hotels and summer cottages all along Barnegat Bay.

We don't know if news of the shark attack in Sea Bright just twelve days before had reached Seaside. The attack was forty miles north, and the fledgling radio service was inconsistent in its local news coverage. It is likely that most did not think about sharks as they headed to the beach that day.

The Burke family of Trenton, New Jersey, were spending a few days in Seaside enjoying the beaches, the food and the amusements. Their young daughter, Verna, was anxious to ride the famous Dentzel carousel, while Charles, their eighteen-year-old son, just wanted to go swimming.

The afternoon found the entire Burke family at the beach. Mr. Burke, dressed in a woolen tunic and short swim outfit, sat on a chaise reading the paper. Mrs. Burke, who had an eye for fashion, strolled at the water's edge wearing a matching swimming ensemble as her young daughter. While Verna played in the surf, her mother kept a watchful eye on her antics.

Charles had met up with two of his school chums, Endell Fenton and Edgar Burkett, soon after arriving in Seaside. The trio headed off to the

Modesty was still the norm in 1926 on New Jersey beaches. *Historical postcard, authors' collection.*

beach earlier than the rest of the family. By the time the Burkes settled on the sand, the boys had already swam out to the sandbar some distance off the beach. They exchanged waves with the family and then began swimming toward the oncoming breakers.

The sight of the trio heading away from shore caught the lifeguard's attention. He stood on the chair and blew his whistle while waving to them to return closer to the beach. The ocean was a bit choppy that day, and there was a definite undertow. When there was no response, he repeated his motions, urging the boys to return to the sandbar.

About that time, the guards noticed that one of the boys was thrashing about and screaming for help. Endell heard the screams for help and bulleted through the water to his friend's side. He couldn't read the horror on Charles's face until he saw the great snout and teeth clenched onto his friend's arm. Fenton grabbed ahold and attempted to pull Charles to safety, but the great beast jerked his prize away and dove into the depths.

The screams were still echoing as the lifeguards sprang into action. Two began to swim toward the site, while two others manned the rescue boat and rushed through the surf toward the attack. Bathers came to join in the search for the missing teenager. Even his parents were in the water shouting his name. Members of the Coast Guard scoured the area for some trace of either the shark or the missing boy. But there was no sign of either.

The next morning, the Coast Guard discovered the body of Charles Burke washed up on a nearby beach just north of town. Even though the corpse was both headless and limbless and a witness reported to have seen the shark attacking the teenager, the coroner gave the cause of death as drowning. This discrepancy does not come as a surprise; over the years, shark attacks have been frequently unreported or downplayed at the behest of local beach resorts.

The town was abuzz with news of the shark attack for the next few days. Sightings of a trio of sharks in the area circulated throughout the community, and bathers stayed closer to the shore than normal. No sharks were caught in the vicinity, and so the guilty shark was never identified or captured.

1928–1931

AUGUST 24, 1928

OFFSHORE NEW JERSEY, NJSAF #29

August 1928 was a busy season for the fishermen of the Jersey shore. The working boats were seen moving out toward the banks in the predawn hours and returning to the docks some hours later, heavily laden with their daily catch. Recreational fishermen, too, joined the parade of vessels as both private and chartered fishing boats jockeyed for position at docks and marinas.

Like many men with a love for saltwater fishing, Charles McNutley was a frequent visitor to the Jersey shore. Although he lived in Philadelphia, he went ocean fishing at least once a fortnight. He was seen in the area so often that many thought him to be a local. He was such a frequent patron of one specific charter boat that the captain made him an honorary crew member.

With Labor Day only a week away, McNutley decided to make a long weekend of his trip to the shore. He arrived late Thursday evening and was standing at the dock waiting for the crew to arrive the following morning. After the usual exchange of pleasantries, he boarded along with the crew and set about organizing and setting up his fishing station. The crew disclosed to him that one customer had landed a fifty-pound striper earlier in the week. That is all McNutley needed to hear; now he was determined to catch a prize fish that day.

McNutley considered himself to be both an expert and congenial fisherman. He always came prepared with his treasured rod and reel, extra tackle, bait and a large hamper full of food. It wasn't that he had a huge appetite; rather, he enjoyed sharing his extra sandwiches, fruit and cakes with the crew.

There were only a few other fishermen on the charter that morning. After introductions and a short conversation about the kinds of fish running, McNutley retired to his station to prepare his equipment. He carefully threaded the heavy-duty line through the guides on the hefty rod and, at the end, secured a large hook.

By the time they reached the fishing banks, McNutley was settled in his favorite position near the stern. Once the anchor was dropped, he baited his line with a wiggling mackerel and cast it into the water. He settled in for what he thought might be a long wait.

The whine of the fishing line whizzing from his reel brought McNutley to his feet. He grabbed the rod with both hands and yanked upward. He thought he could feel the tug as the hook embedded into the fish's mouth.

Clutching the rod with one hand, he tried to reel in the fish. It felt as though he had caught something very large, as it was stronger than anything he had ever hooked before. Each time McNutley thought he had it near the surface, it would suddenly jerk away and plunge into the depths, ripping away yards and yards of heavy line.

By now, he was sweating profusely and beginning to tire. At last the fish ceased its struggling and seemed to accept its inevitable capture. Within a few minutes, he had brought his catch to the surface.

Gasps spread along the deck. But no one was more shocked than McNutley; he had caught a seven-foot shark. Before everyone got a good look at it, the creature began to thrash about and slam itself against the side of the boat. The vessel quivered as it hammered the hull with its great head. Water sprayed across the deck, and tackle scattered in every direction. Although the crew thrust harpoons into the frenzied shark, it was to no avail. The captain finally arrived and quickly dispatched the creature with five pistol shots to its head.

Because of its size, the shark was netted and lashed to the side of the boat for the remainder of the day. When they arrived back on shore, the crew assisted McNutley gutting the seven-foot-long creature. After they sawed off the head and tail, McNutley used a sturdy butcher's knife to slice open the torso, allowing organs and intestines to spew from the cavity. Then one crewman jabbed at the bloated stomach lying among the viscera,

Hauling a shark onboard is tricky business, even if it is a juvenile. *Courtesy of the Library of Congress.*

rupturing the membrane. It contained partially digested food and a cleanly severed human thumb. Closer inspection of the appendage revealed that it was attached to a fragment of dark blue fabric. No other human body parts were found.

McNutley found himself the center of attention as news of the discovery spread along the shore. Everyone, land lovers and fishermen alike, seemed to have an opinion about the origin of the thumb. But among the seafaring community, the consensus was that the fabric was from a merchant marine uniform.

Charles McNutley continued coming to the shore for many more years to go fishing. Although he caught large stripers, sea bass and even a tuna, he never again caught a shark.

The identity of the thumb's owner was never discovered, so we can only assume that somewhere there was a merchant marine sailor who was missing his left thumb. Of the shark, we only know that its last meal included a human digit.

NOVEMBER 18, 1928

ONE AND A HALF MILES OFF SEA BRIGHT, NJSAF #30

November 18, 1928, was a mild day for November. Although there had been a light snowfall a few days before, the temperatures were in the mid-forties that morning. The breeze off the ocean, however, was from the north, bringing an icy chill that forced anyone working outside to bundle up.

The pre-dawn hours found three local fishermen—Charles Anderson, Emit Lindberg and Oscar Benson—aboard their Jersey skiff heading through choppy waters toward the fishing grounds a mile and a half off Sea Bright. These were familiar waters, as this was a daily trek for the trio when the schools of cod were migrating. The men knew the hazards of the North Atlantic in the winter and were well prepared.

The evening before, the three had meticulously inspected and repaired their most essential piece of gear: their cod nets. They had arrived that morning dressed in multiple layers of woolen clothes topped with well-worn oilskin slickers. As cod fishing was difficult and sometimes dangerous work, they bore extra provisions, as well as several thermoses of coffee and heavy thermal work gloves.

The three fishermen had been friends for many years. They had fished together for so long that they worked like a well-oiled machine. The outbound trip was uneventful. They discussed the weather, the tides and the price of cod at the market.

As they approached the fishing grounds, the men scoured the surface of the water looking for signs of fish. Anderson, captain of the skiff, wasted no time in maneuvering into position. Without speaking, the men immediately but carefully released their net into the water off the portside, watching as it sank beneath the water. Then they began the long, slow trawl toward shore.

It wasn't long before the skiff shifted abruptly to port. It felt as if the net was overloaded with fish. Could they be that lucky to have filled the net so quickly? They began pulling in the nets, slowly and deliberately. At first, they found only a few junk fish, and then there was nothing. The men's faces took on furtive frowns. As the net cleared the surface, the flailing and thrashing grew stronger.

Then the cry went out, "Shark!" That exclamation is never a good sign to fishermen. Sharks will eat the bait and chase away the catch. Worst of all, they become entangled in the expensive fishing nets and can rupture the vital and expensive gear.

Fishermen discussing politics in 1928. Their camaraderie superseded any personal political leanings. *Historical postcard, authors' collection.*

As the men yanked the nets alongside, a giant tail reached out and slammed against the hull. Before they could react, a second tail emerged from the wiggling mass and slammed a glancing blow against Oscar, knocking him to the deck. There were not one, but two large bluenose sharks entangled in their net, and the frenzied beasts were not about to give up.

There was no time to discuss tactics. With two sharks trapped inside their precious net, not only was today's catch a loss, but their indispensable cod net might be destroyed. Meanwhile, the skiff danced and jostled across the water surface uncontrollably as the pair of giants thrashed and rammed and hammered on the hull. Unless they acted quickly, the men would lose not only the boat but their very lives as well.

The captain attempted to maneuver the skiff into position to enable the others to harpoon and gaff the attackers. It took nearly an hour of maneuvering in the choppy waters, and then the first harpoons missed their mark. The enraged beasts increased their vengeance on the wooden skiff. The men battled the sharks for what seemed like hours, stabbing them relentlessly while the captain struggled to keep the boat afloat.

At last the giants lay motionless alongside. The skiff bobbed gently in the water; the men stood along the side staring down into the bulging net. Despite the frigid wind, sweat ran down their faces and bathed their many cuts and bruises. It had been more than two hours, and they had gaffed and harpooned the sharks at least twenty-eight times.

Although tedious and tiresome, mending the nets is an essential part of a fisherman's duties. *Courtesy of the Library of Congress.*

But the job was not over. They secured the net containing the pair of sharks to the side of the skiff and made for port. Too tired to talk, they rode in silence back to shore, staring at the two brutes that had refused to die.

It wasn't until they reached the dock that they noticed their own wounds. Even then, their injuries had to wait until they had carefully disposed of the sharks and inspected their precious nets for damage. The trio considered themselves lucky. The skiff received minor damage on the port side just above the waterline, the men had an assortment of cuts and abrasion, and with a bit of work, the net could be repaired.

There was no payday on that eighteenth of November, but the crew came home safely. They would mend the damaged net, repair the hull of the skiff and be back on the water the next morning in search of cod. The two bull sharks would no longer troll these waters in search of codfish or unsuspecting fishermen.

JULY 15, 1931

SEA GIRT, NJSAF #31

The year 1931 was one many Americans would like to forget. Two years into the Great Depression, times were hard. Millions were out of work, wages were cut and, despite the optimism of President Hoover, few could see a light at the end of the tunnel.

In the early spring, as banks closed and businesses went bankrupt, the Congress made "The Star-Spangled Banner" the official national anthem of the country. Although most folks, including the military, had used it for decades, Washington politicians debated at length. As a result, many thought Congress should be spending its time creating jobs and feeding the hungry, not debating a piece of sheet music.

Americans did everything they could to cope with the economic crisis. Those who could, planted gardens in any patch of land that would grow a crop. Many of those with jobs had their salaries cut; others lost their only source of income and could no longer house or feed their families.

Among those struggling to feed an extended family was a young man who had joined the local national guard about the time of the stock market crash. After his job was cut, the stipend that he earned as a member of the New Jersey National Guard was his way to put food on the table. He volunteered for any job or duty offered. As a result, he was encamped with the 113th Infantry on the grounds of the training center in Sea Girt in the summer of 1931.

During the warm months of the year, the guardsmen lived in canvas tents lined up in neat rows on the parade grounds adjacent to the beach. It was hot and humid despite the ocean breezes, and when it rained, the grounds were a muddy quagmire.

Most of the guardsmen thought themselves lucky to at least be bringing home some money in these hard times. They went about their duties with enthusiasm, laughing and joking with one another, developing an intense brotherly camaraderie.

On July 15, the infantry practiced for hours, doing what the infantry does best: march. The drills were exhausting in the oppressive heat, making it difficult to maintain synchronized cadence. When at last the men were dismissed, they headed to the mess tent. Making fun of the food was part of the ritual in guard life, yet everyone ate their fill.

Those assigned to sentry duties that evening took up their posts, and those lucky enough to be off duty headed down to the beach for a swim. It was nearly dusk as they waded into the surf. One after another they plunged into the briny waves and swam away from the shore. Instantly, the cool surf washed away the sweat of the day and eased their aching muscles.

As they headed back toward the beach, one guardsman suddenly yowled out in pain. Instinctively, the others rushed toward him. At first, they thought he had just stepped on something sharp on the bottom. But when he stepped clear of the surf, they could see blood trickling from a laceration just above his ankle. Although he insisted that a large fish had bitten him, there was a lively debate about what had attacked the soldier. Finally, one by one they inspected the wound and agreed that it was indeed a shark bite.

They offered to take him to sickbay, but he quickly refused. He didn't want to go on sick call and lose a day's pay. The men applied pressure to the wound, and before long, it stopped bleeding. Everyone agreed that the injury was superficial; no one would report the incident.

The "citizen soldier" did indeed have a close call. Fortunately, his only souvenir of the encounter with the shark was a small scar just above his ankle. Both the young man and his attacker would live yet another day—the soldier to march the parade grounds of Sea Girt, and the shark to prowl the beaches of the Jersey shore.

AUGUST 6, 1931

FORT HANCOCK/SANDY HOOK, NJSAF #32

This second shark attack of the summer of 1931 took place just three weeks after the Sea Girt attack and also involved a member of the military. This time, the attack took place at Fort Hancock, the Coastal Artillery Defense post located in Sandy Hook.

During the years of the Great Depression, the U.S. Army was busy upgrading the facility. The soldiers, both enlisted men as well as officers, came from all over the nation. Although a few might have been drafted, many chose to enlist. Some did so for strictly patriotic reasons, while others did so because they could think of no other way to feed their families.

The army was especially popular with men from the Midwest, where jobs were nonexistent and the price of farm produce crashed, putting many

farmers out of business. Military service was a viable option in these difficult times. The soldier got clothing, lodging, medical care and three squares a day. His allotment was sent home to put a bit of food on the table. As meager as the pay was, it was better than nothing.

Army life was hard and sometimes boring, but it was a living, and they never missed a meal. The troops had duty six days a week with time for recreational activities. During the summer, the beach became the popular pastime. They threw footballs across the dunes, jogged the wide corridors of sandy beach and swam in the playful waters of the Atlantic.

That August morning began like any other. The sky was still covered in clouds at dawn as the reveille echoed across Sandy Hook. But as the sun rose in the sky, it burned off the haze, and by mid-morning, Fort Hancock was basking under a bright summer sky.

Thursday was a workday for most of the troops. One squad of artillery gunners, however, had the good fortune to be off duty that morning. They knew that hanging around the barracks was a bad idea. Their sergeant would undoubtedly find some "urgent" task that required immediate attention, and if a soldier wasn't careful, he could turn into a latrine queen in a flash.

As soon as breakfast was over, the squad headed out for a swim. A blustery ocean breeze whipped at their fatigues as they plowed barefoot over the dunes to the sandy beach. It was the perfect day to be off duty.

One young man from Ohio, known as Buckeye, seemed in awe of Sandy Hook. Although others made fun of him, he often collected shells and sea glass, which he kept in an old sock in his locker. Once he paid another soldier to take pictures of the beach and then carefully packaged them and mailed them home to Ohio.

When they arrived at the beach, Buckeye stood on the sand, allowing the quartz crystals to ooze through his toes as he stared out across the water to the horizon. When he looked back at the beach, the others were already swimming. He tossed off his shirt and ran into the surf, leaping over the first wave. He stretched his arms forward into a dive. Within seconds, he emerged from the water right beside his old bunkmate, Murphy. The two swam out and joined the others in the briny water just beyond the breakers.

Everyone was laughing and joking when Buckeye saw a dark shadow beneath the surface scoot past him. He called out, "Man! Look at this big fish!" Just then, the shadow spun about and made straight for him. As the others watched in horror, Buckeye heaved forward in the water. A stifled gurgling sound escaped his throat as he went under water for a moment. He

A historical postcard illustrates a somewhat comical interpretation of a shark encounter. *Historical postcard, authors' collection.*

popped back up, yelping in pain. It felt as if a giant pair of pliers was locked onto his leg and trying to pull him downward.

Within seconds, Murphy had wrapped his arms around Buckeye's chest, holding his head above the water. "It bit me, that big fish bit me!" the Ohioan shrieked. The entire squad moved as a single unit, latching onto Buckeye. They made a hasty retreat to the beach as a thin trail of blood traced their path through the surf and onto the sand.

By the time they reached the shore, blood was spewing from two large punctures on both sides of his left leg. The blood ran down his calves and pooled on his foot, turning it cherry red. The squad quickly applied pressure to his wounds and bound them tightly with a shirt. Scooping him up, they jogged double-time to the infirmary.

The wound was cleaned, sutured and bandaged. After visits by several officers, it was positively identified as a shark bite. Long before Buckeye was bandaged, word of the attack had spread across the base. By noon, Colonel Johnson, base commander, had banned swimming on the oceanside of the Hook until further notice.

The young soldier from Ohio was "put on quarters" for a few days and didn't go into the water the remainder of the summer. He spent his downtime listening to baseball on the radio and collecting shells and sea glass for his mother. He would need no other souvenirs to remind him of his time at Fort Hancock; those two jagged scars on his left leg would be with him forever.

AUGUST 27, 1931

SEA BRIGHT/OFF TWIN LIGHTS, NJSAF #33

This third shark incident of the summer of 1931 took place just three weeks after the attack on the soldier at Fort Hancock in early August. It occurred in the same general vicinity, a mile southeast of Sandy Hook. But this time, the incident involved a local chief of police and his fishing buddy.

Friday, August 27, marked the final summer weekend before the Labor Day holiday. Nels Jacobson, the Sea Bright chief of police, and his friend Franklin Covert were poised for a busy weekend ahead. Both prominent locals, the men hoped that the beaches would be crowded and that tourists would come for that final summer visit. Crowds had declined during the Depression, and local businesses had suffered. One decent weekend before the end of summer would surely help the spirits around Sea Bright.

Being avid fishermen, the two took every opportunity they could to spend the day on the water. For the last few days, local fishermen recounted stories of their encounters with bluefish just off the Twin Lights area. The two friends were anxious to get out on the water and bring home some of those trophy-sized fish.

That Friday morning, the sky was overcast and the ocean listless. Both men had taken the day off from work and were at the dock loading their supplies onto their well-worn Sea Bright skiff long before the sun rose. They brought everything they would need, including their rods, wire leaders, sturdy hooks and, of course, the essential for blue fishing: a "blues billy." The small wooden club was used to subdue the thrashing aggressive fish once it was on board.

They left the dock in Sea Bright and, once in the channel, sped up the inlet toward the bay. They were just clearing the tip of the hook as the sun peeked over the horizon. With Covert at the helm, the skiff skimmed the water heading southeast into the rising sun. As soon as there was enough light, Jacobson began scanning the waters for schools of fish. Bluefish are dawn feeders, and the men knew that sighting schools of baitfish meant that the bluefish would not be far away.

The moment that Covert saw the telltale bubbling water, the men snatched their rods and cast them into the midst of the school of baitfish. It didn't take long before the unmistakable whine of the line being ripped from the reel brought Jacobson to his feet. He grasped onto the leather grip and pulled skyward with all his might. The hook was set.

As he clutched the rod with both hands, it began to bend downward toward the water. Jacobson took a step backward. He yanked on the rod with his left arm as he struggled to crank the heavy reel with the other. Slowly but surely, the line was forced back onto the reel as the fish came closer to the surface. For some time, the battle continued, as the fish fought to shake off the hook. Jacobson held his ground, reeling in the line inch by inch, bringing the fish closer and closer to the boat.

Finally, there was a great splash as the indignant animal threw itself into the air before crashing back into the water in one last effort to escape. The two men shouted in unison, and Jacobson began tugging the fish across the surface of the water toward the skiff.

Just then, a dark streamlined shape surged from the depths, taking aim at the hapless bluefish. It broke through the water and lunged at their catch. At that moment, Jacobson yanked on the line, and the shark missed its target and crashed into the side of the skiff.

Jacobson looked into the huge eye of the behemoth, and then its giant teeth flashed inches from his hands. He dropped his rod and grabbed ahold of the gunwale. As the skiff bounced and wobbled across the water, the men reached for the nearest weapon. Jacobson grabbed a gaff as Covet took up the ever-handy "blues billy" and quickly dispatched the intruder.

They measured the carcass of the bluenose and found it to be eleven and a half feet long, more than half the length of their skiff. He was certainly not the fish they were after that morning. Although it cost them a good rod, and one good-sized bluefish, neither fisherman was injured in the fray.

CHAPTER 7

1932–1936

JUNE 26, 1932

OCEAN CITY, NJSAF #34

Although the New Year is usually a festive time, the arrival of 1932 brought little jubilation to most Americans. With over fifteen million unemployed and entire families living in their cars traveling around the country searching for work, there was no light at the end of the tunnel of the nationwide Depression. It was an election year, one filled with controversy, discontent and a growing hopefulness that the young New York governor, Franklin D. Roosevelt, might somehow pull us out of this quagmire.

That summer, the tourist industry faltered along the Jersey shore, putting thousands more out of work. Not even the excitement of June 6, when Lou Gehrig hit four home runs in a single game, could lift local spirits.

Such was the case along the eight-mile-long barrier island known as Ocean City, once called Peck's Island. A group of Methodist ministers purchased the island in 1879 and turned it into a Christian retreat and camp meeting site. Advertised as a "moral community," the island prohibited public drinking, lewdness of any sort and unchristian-like behaviors. It wasn't long before Ocean City became a year-round coastal settlement that flourished until the crash of 1929.

Like most Americans, the good folks of Ocean City did whatever they could to survive and feed their families. People took any job available, and

even the smallest parcels of land were used to grow vegetables. As in other shore towns, many locals turned to the sea in search for food.

One such man, Giavanno Giacomo, had lived in Ocean City his entire life. Although Giavanno was not yet twenty-one, he was a responsible son who did whatever he could to bring home a bit of money and food for the family table. Each morning, Giavanno and his younger brother, Lorenzo, took the old family gillnetting boat out to the fishing grounds a few miles offshore in search of fish.

Their aged boat, the *Mia Bella*, had been in the family for some years, but it wasn't until recently that the two brothers had repaired the wooden hull and equipped the twenty-five-foot vessel with a hand-cranked net drum. With this large wooden reel at the stern, they began gillnet fishing in the age-old method of their Mediterranean ancestors.

Using the netting they found in their grandfather's shed, they mended panels and then re-strung the weighted rope lines and headers. So far, it had worked well. The brothers were able to supply fresh seafood to their mother each day, with which she made huge batches of stew for their evening meals. It may have been monotonous, but it was always a hearty meal. When the fishing was good, they would also sell enough at the market to help the family survive for another week or two.

That Sunday morning, June 26, found Giavanno and his brother aboard the old wooden craft. As soon as they had checked their fuel supply and sorted and arranged the gill netting, Giavanno slid the throttle forward, and the *Mia Bella* surged out into the open waters of the Atlantic heading for the fishing grounds a few miles offshore.

When they reached the banks, they paused the engine and began the laborious task of reeling the nets off the stern of the boat in careful succession. Once the panels were fully immersed, Giavanno gently pushed the throttle and they began a slow sweep forward, with the net trailing off the stern. The brothers took a bit of a rest, sipping coffee from their thermoses and sharing their hopes for a hefty catch. At first, Giavanno didn't notice the strain on the boat's engine; it was far too early for the net to be full. But as the drag on the boat became more obvious, he looked up at Lorenzo, and the two exchanged knowing smiles. It could only mean one thing: they had hit a large school of fish. This could mean a good payday after all.

They raced to take their positions and began reeling in the yards and yards of net on the giant drum. The weight of the net was extraordinary. Fish began to tumble onto the deck in groups of two or three, but nothing so far looked like a huge school. Yet the net remained abnormally heavy.

Sharks are frequently entrapped within commercial fishing nets. The result usually is damaged critical fishing equipment and, typically, the death of the hapless shark. *Courtesy NOAA Central Library Historical Fisheries.*

After what seemed like an eternity, the net was pulled up against the stern. The two brothers, their arms aching and with sweat streaming down their faces, leaned over the gunwale and peered into the net. Their eyes widened in horror as an enormous eye, protruding through the net, glared back at them. The massive head of the beast sported a gaping mouth filled with jagged teeth. It was a shark—an enormous shark. As they watched, the massive torso thrashed and flailed, ripping through the netting with its mighty tail. Fish were tossed back into the sea and water sprayed across the stern, drenching the astonished brothers.

Without a moment's hesitation, they each grabbed the first weapon they found and began to pummel the creature. What mattered now was saving the precious fishing nets from further destruction. At last, they laid down the bloody harpoon and gaff and stood staring at the motionless carcass. Although there was no money in sharks these days, they decided to bring it ashore and put it on display. People might pay a couple of cents to get a good look at such an enormous beast.

Once again with considerable grunting, sweating and heaving, they managed to yank the shark onto the boat. It landed on the floor with a ponderous thud. At that moment, it suddenly seemed to regain consciousness, flailing wildly about. It slammed Giavanno with its enormous tail, sending him flying against the gunwale. A searing pain shot through his leg, and he shrieked in agony. Lorenzo grabbed an axe and dispatched the creature with multiple blows to its massive head. At last, the creature lay lifeless in a pool of its own blood.

When Giavanno tried to stand, his ankle couldn't support his weight, and within minutes it ballooned to three times its normal size. Despite the throbbing in his leg, he managed to hobble to the pilot house. He headed for the inlet at full speed while his brother kept watch on the day's surprising catch.

The trip back to shore seemed longer than ever before. The brothers anxiously kept one eye on the approaching shore and the other on the enormous beast splayed across their deck. At last, they reached the inlet and crossed into Egg Harbor Bay. Once inside, they slowed down and maneuvered carefully along the shore until they reached the dock.

Once they arrived, word spread like wildfire. Soon a crowd gathered to marvel at the five-hundred-pound beast. Giavanno, still in excruciating pain, was taken off board and hustled to a local doctor, who set his ankle. He recovered from his encounter with the shark but spent the remainder of the summer hobbling about on crutches.

Although the shark was put on display for a few days, it brought only a pittance for the brothers. It was 1932; even a penny was tough to come by in those days. The identification of the behemoth was not reported, so we remain uncertain of what species of shark broke Giovanno's ankle.

This was the first shark encounter that summer along the Jersey shore, but it would not be the last. In less than forty-eight hours, two more local fishermen would come face to face with another menacing beast.

JUNE 28, 1932

OFF SEA ISLE CITY, NJSAF #35

Tuesday, June 28, 1932, began like any other for the residents of the Jersey shore. It was early in the summer season, yet people had a general sense of foreboding as the listless economy dominated the conversation. Few folks had heard of the shark encounter two days ago in Ocean City, or if they did, they gave it little thought. Most were concentrating on feeding their families and so had more pressing things on their minds.

By this time, many of the commercial fishing boats had gone bankrupt, and those remaining now faced the additional strain of the new federal tax on fuels. For those still holding on, it was critical that every trip offshore bring home a bountiful catch.

The captain of the *Sea Lily* had been fortunate so far. He had inherited the aged fishing boat from his father and so had no mortgage on his craft. It was a side-mounted trawler with crank winches and a net drum near the stern. It's true it showed its age. Its paint had faded, its fixtures were dated and its aged otter trawl netting had been repaired more times than he could count. But the *Sea Lily* was nonetheless a sturdy and reliable craft.

Like many other commercial fishermen, the captain had to cut costs wherever he could. That meant cutting back on the size of his crew. Although he had once kept a four-man crew on the *Sea Lily*, he now employed only two men. Both Antonio Fonzzo and Luke Cestaldi had worked for the captain for a couple of years. They were experienced, hardworking fishermen. The jovial duo was always on time for work, always sober and never needed prompting to complete the job at hand. The two men were gratified to be employed in these tough times. Jobs were scarce to nonexistent, and the captain was a reasonable man who always made the payroll. Upon return from each trip, he allowed Antonio and Luke to each take home enough fish for their dinner. In those days, that was a greatly appreciated fringe benefit.

On that Tuesday morning, the *Sea Lily* and its crew reached the fishing grounds just off Sea Isle City before the sunrise. Antonio and Luke moved about the deck positioning the trawl nets. The captain gave the signal, and the men eased the bulbous-shaped tip of the net, known as the cod end, into the water. As it sank into the depths, they carefully released the long lengths of netting, watching as the weighted bobbins on the foot ropes sank beneath the surface. Finally, only the floats on the head rope could be seen. The winch released more and more netting until even these disappeared.

It was a slow process, but it was very important that the net was immersed correctly so that the boards were holding the wings open, allowing fish to enter and become trapped within the net. Once everything was in place, they gave the signal to the captain, who began slowly edging the *Sea Lily* forward at a smooth and steady speed.

Although it would take some time for the net to do its work, the men waited and remained vigilant. The sun rose higher in the sky and the day grew warmer, and at last the captain gave the order to haul in the net. Luke and Antonio took their positions along the side. Today, Luke manned the winch and Antonio began guiding the incoming net into neat furrows to prevent it from tangling. It was backbreaking work, so every so often, Antonio and Luke would trade positions for a while. By now, a few fish caught in the outer netting flopped unceremoniously onto the deck. Antonio scooped them up, tossing the good ones into the holding box and lobbing the bycatch back into the water.

At last the floats on the headline appeared once more. Luke cranked the old winch, drawing it closer and closer to the boat. Although the cod end was near, it was still too soon to tell if it had been a successful trip. When it finally came into sight, the bulbous cod end seemed to be bursting with fish.

What appears to be a hearty catch may turn out to be a dangerous shark encounter, should an apex predator be trapped within the net. *Courtesy NOAA Central Library Historical Fisheries.*

At long last, the headrope was pulled taut, which brought the cod end up out of the water. It was bulging with silvery wiggling fish. As soon as they swung the globular mass onto the deck, Antonio reached over and released the holding knot. Hundreds of fish erupted from the opening, flopping every which way across the deck.

Just then the massive torso of a shark emerged from the heap of wiggling fish, just inches away from the two fishermen. A shared expletive echoed across the deck as the two reached for the nearest weapons. Fish were flopping every which way as the giant beast, still entangled in the netting, thrashed and lurched frantically trying to escape. The shark slammed its body against the deck, causing the boat to ricochet across the water as the giant tail swung back and forth, smashing the holding box of fish and sending it overboard in a hail of splinters.

Suddenly, the shark jerked sideways, and before Antonio could move away, it opened its mouth and sunk its huge jagged teeth into his knee.

Although he shrieked in pain, the shark would not let go. Luke was at his side in an instant, thrusting his knife into the eye of the menacing beast. Antonio screamed relentlessly as Luke stabbed the shark over and over until it released its grip on his friend. Finally, the great fish lay lifeless and bloody on the deck.

By then, the captain had cut the engine and hurried aft to help. He inspected Antonio's leg, pulled off his shirt and used it to apply pressure to the wound. Although he managed to slow the bleeding, it did nothing to alleviate the fisherman's excruciating pain.

The captain directed Luke to maintain constant pressure on the wound as he rushed to the wheel and headed the *Sea Lily* to the nearest port. Once back on land, Antonio was rushed to the nearest local doctor, who quickly arranged for him to be taken to a Philadelphia hospital for more extensive treatment.

Antonio survived his encounter with the shark. He had surgery and remained hospitalized for more than a week. Although he would eventually recover from the vicious wound, he would carry the hideous scars for the remainder of his life.

AUGUST 10, 1932

OFF MANTOLOKING, NJSAF #36

By the summer of 1932, the once vibrant commercial fishing industry of the Jersey shore was in tatters, destroyed by the ever-growing winds of the worldwide Depression. Although many boats of the fleet had been lost to creditors, a few hearty fishermen remained, trying to eke out a living.

Alfred Larson was captain of the seventy-foot fishing trawler the *Min Fiskebat*. Having worked on fishing boats ever since he was a young boy, he knew this section of the Atlantic like the back of his hand. Now with his own vessel, he trawled the waters for the Bay Head Fishery, just three miles south of Point Pleasant.

The *Min Fiskebat* was a well-built and sturdy craft that held its own against both bad weather and rough seas. Captain Larson had kept the same crew on the *Min Fiskebat* for the last two years. The six men were experienced and hardworking. The captain was strict about work ethic, being sober and pulling one's own weight yet was a pleasant enough employer.

Two of his crew, John Olsen and Olaf Larson, were fellow Scandinavians. History doesn't tell us if Olaf Larson was related to the captain, although

some speculate that he was a nephew. The two men knew that their shared ancestry likely helped them secure their jobs. But they also knew that they could, and would, be easily replaced if they failed to perform. There were dozens of men on the dock just waiting for an opening aboard the *Min Fiskebat*.

August 10, 1932, began like any other day. The predawn air lay heavy across the shore as the fishermen hurried to the dock to begin a day's work aboard the old trawler. Being late was never an option for the crew; in fact, it was considered good form to be there waiting for the arrival of the captain. Being tardy meant looking for another job.

The light was just beginning to tease the horizon as the *Min Fiskebat* slipped away from the dock. Upon reaching the open ocean, the captain laid a course for the fishing banks some distance offshore near Mantoloking.

When they were well offshore, the captain gave the signal and the men sprang into action, scurrying about the deck, arranging nets, securing clips, checking latches and laying out lines into precise positions. With a nod, the captain ordered the net to be lowered into the water. The great winches on the stern began to creak, allowing the string of giant pulleys to release the net gently into the sea.

The first mate gave a shout, and the captain began to slowly increase the speed of the *Min Fiskebat*. For the next two hours, the crew remained vigilant, watching for glitches in the netting as the boat moved slowly but steadily across the water.

Finally, the command "haul in" was shouted from the pilot house, and the crew of six sprang into action once again. They manned the winches, stabilized the pulleys and gently but firmly guided the net closer and closer to the ship. At first, everything went along normally as hundreds of yards of loosely woven netting were reeled into the stern.

Suddenly, the first mate bellowed, "Stop!" The winches and pulleys screeched to a halt. He leaned over the stern and peered at the emerging net. Something just didn't look right. Although they could make out fish wiggling and squirming within the net, the net appeared more elongated than usual. With a wave of the mate's hand, the winches once again began drawing the netting closer to the stern.

When it was in position, the pulleys went into action and the net rose from the depths. Streams of sea water cascaded from the mounds of wiggling silvery fish as the hoist arm swung around and gently deposited the net on the deck. There was a shout of glee: it was a huge catch!

It was then that Olaf realized that something was very wrong. A large part of the net wasn't wiggling at all; it was thrashing and bouncing about all on

The business end of a shark, revealing its mouthful of razor-sharp teeth. *Courtesy NOAA Central Library Historical Fisheries.*

its own. There was something large caught within the net. Before he could speak, the net was unfastened, spewing thousands of fish across the deck.

It's hard to say who first saw the single bulging eye poking through the net. Great jagged teeth began frantically shredding the net and the great body slammed against the deck over and over as the entire craft creaked and moaned in protest. It was a shark—a very large shark.

The crew ran for weapons while others shoved piles of fish into the hold away from the intruder. For a few moments, the shark did not move. Olaf pulled the net away from its huge caudal fin as another crewman set to lasso the appendage. Suddenly, the shark swung its tail forward, smacking Olaf mid-torso and sending him flying over the rail into the ocean.

While two crew members ran to his aid, the others pelted the beast with whatever they could find. Finally, the great shark lay motionless, blood streaming down its gigantic head. But when John pulled the netting away, the shark lunged at him, clamping down onto his boot with its ragged teeth. In an instant, it ripped the boot into two pieces. Blood squirted from John's wound and spilled down his leg onto the deck.

Captain Larson appeared, and ended the fray by dispatching the shark with a shotgun blast directly into its huge bulging eye. For a moment, they stood in silent amazement. It was an enormous beast—eighteen feet long and a whopping 1,800 pounds. The *Min Fiskebat* hurried back to the dock to salvage the catch and repair the damaged net. By sunrise the following morning, the trawler and its crew were once again lowering their nets in the waters off Mantoloking.

JUNE 19, 1935

WILDWOOD, NJSAF #37

The summer of 1935 was plagued not only by one of the worst heat waves in recorded history but also by rumors from Europe of the growing threat from Adolph Hitler. America's breadbasket, the Central Plains, suffered a devastating dust storm and drought. Along the Atlantic coast, the stifling heat continued unabated.

On June 19, the crew of the *Nautilus* prepared the trawler for the day's search for bluefish off the shore of Wildwood. The captain was thirty-one-year-old Manuel Chalor. He was admittedly quite young to be a ship's captain. Some would say he just got lucky, but others would insist it was his expertise as a fisherman and his competence handling his crew that earned him the title.

Earning a spot as a crewman on the *Nautilus* was a much sought-after job. Despite being about the same age as his crew, Manuel Chalor maintained his crew's respect by his honest and forthright manner. He not only insisted that the crew call him by his first name but was also a hands-on boss who frequently took on the most difficult or dangerous tasks himself.

On that June morning, the ship was berthed at Otten Harbor in Wildwood. Before mid-morning, the *Nautilus* was fifty some miles offshore. The crew had begun to reel in the great trawler nets when there was an odd clunking sound and the wenches groaned to a halt. The crew inspected the onboard mechanics and found everything to be in working order. Captain Chalor joined the crew as they inspected their equipment and agreed it could only mean that something was ensnaring the weighted bobbins on the bottom rope line of the net. The problem had to be investigated and perhaps even extricated by hand.

The captain immediately ordered the dory lowered into the water along the starboard side of the ship. Although several crew members volunteered for the difficult task, the captain said he would take care of it himself. As the crew launched the dory, he gave instructions to the first mate and crew and then grabbed a few tools and a knife. He glanced over the side of the ship, grabbed onto the rope ladder and quickly slid down to the awaiting boat.

Chalor eased himself onto the seat of the dory facing the stern. He pushed away from the *Nautilus*, letting the boat drift about twenty feet from the ship before he grabbed ahold of the oars. Using the rowlock, he swung

the oars into position and spread the flat sides of the blades toward the water. He leaned back, sweeping the oars toward the stern, propelling the small boat forward.

He had just begun his second stroke of the oars when he caught a glimpse of something in the water ahead. It was huge and speeding straight for him. Before he could call out, the huge gray shark vaulted skyward. For a split second, it seemed to be suspended in midair directly over his head. Then it plunged downward, landing with a great wallop across the width of the dory, pinning him against the side with its massive torso.

The giant beast thrashed and convulsed, snapping its huge ragged teeth every which way. The boat shuddered and wobbled uncontrollably as the captain's shrieks echoed over the curses and shouts of the crew. The shark curled its snout toward the captain menacingly, as if blaming him for its predicament. Although the huge mouth chomped closer and closer toward him, Captain Chalor continued to beat on the shark with his fists. The crew pummeled the beast with hunks of lumber, iron and even pieces of gear and tools. When some of the projectiles aimed for the shark hit the beleaguered skipper, he snatched them up and used them to pound on the beast's snout.

A sudden deafening scream of agony rose above all the shouting as the shark latched onto Chalor's right arm. Its jagged teeth traced the length of his arm, leaving an open laceration from his shoulder to his elbow. Before the echo had died down, a second blood-curdling scream filled the air as the great beast ripped off four of the captain's fingers with a single chomp of its teeth.

At that moment, a crewman planted his harpoon directly into the head of the frenzied beast. The shark wrenched itself upward and then fell back onto the side of the boat. Nearly capsized, the dory began to fill with water. The shark tumbled backward and sank into the sea. Within seconds, it had disappeared completely. The dory popped back upward with the wounded captain clinging to the side.

Two crewmen leapt into the water and quickly brought the captain back on board, where they struggled to slow the bleeding. He remained alert and able to order the ship to head for port before falling into unconsciousness.

The first mate took command and returned the *Nautilus* to Otten's Harbor, where Manuel Chalor was rushed to Mace Hospital in Wildwood for treatment. The large laceration on his arm required several dozen stitches before it was wrapped, and the stubs of his four amputated fingers were cleaned and bandaged.

After treatment, he insisted on returning to his ship, despite the physician's objections. Although the doctors stipulated that he return each day for at least a week and have the wounds checked and cleaned, he returned only once. The young captain relied mostly on home remedies for the healing and whiskey for the pain.

The *Nautilus*, with both its young skipper and crew, quickly returned to the sea, where they continued to fish for blues. Captain Chalor remained quite philosophical about the whole thing; after all, he reflected, the only reason he had crossed paths with the shark was because they were both hunting the same prey. It was an accident, or as the *New York Times* would report, the shark had simply "miscalculated."

JUNE 12, 1936

LONG BRANCH, NJSAF #38

The year 1936 was the eighth year of the Depression. Roosevelt's numerous work projects and relief programs had decreased the unemployment rate from 30 to less than 10 percent. The Social Security Act had been passed, it was an election year and there was an air of expectancy across the nation.

After a late spring, summer finally arrived with a vengeance in New Jersey. People flocked to the beach in search of cooling ocean breezes and a chance to soak away their cares in the soothing Atlantic surf.

On the morning of June 12, the local church bells of Long Branch welcomed the faithful under a bright cloudless sky. At the same time, two local fishermen, Saul White and Charles Dillione, arrived at the dock prepared for a day of fishing. They had their favorite boat rods, heavy tackle and a large container of ripe chum. Of course, they brought some sandwiches and a couple bottles of what Charlie liked to call "liquid refreshment."

The weather-worn fishing boat bobbed gently in the water as the two loaded their gear onboard. *Miss Ruby* was twenty-two feet in length with an engine house midship that divided the stern from the bow. Over the years, they had relied on the aged but sturdy craft for countless trips to the fishing banks offshore.

As soon as they reached the fishing grounds, Saul set up his gear in the stern while Charlie opted to establish his post in the bow. Charlie began heaving great buckets full of bloody chum into the water. As the slick floated

away from the boat, they hurried to their positions and cast their lines into the center of the fetid layer. Before long, they had nearly filled their keepers with pan-size blues.

Around three o'clock, Saul was leaning against the stern, staring out across the water. Suddenly, the tip of his rod bent, and the drag began clicking slowly as the line inched away from the reel. A grin spread across his face. The tug on the line told him something had taken the bait. Just as he jerked his rod skyward to set the hook, line screamed off his spool as the fish raced away with the hook securely embedded in its mouth.

Saul could tell that this was not just a small bluefish; he had caught something very large. He allowed the fish to run, taking as much line as it needed. Then when it paused to rest, he spun the handle of his reel as fast as he could, retrieving yards and yards of fishing line. The game continued for some time until at last the fish was exhausted. Saul knew he could bring it to the surface now.

Just as he got his first glimpse of the ten-pound bluefish, he spied the telltale dorsal fin torpedo through the water heading straight for the stern. Then there was a giant thud and the boat shuddered. Saul dropped his rod. When he raised his eyes, all he could see was the torso of a massive shark. It was enormous, nearly as wide as the boat. The uninvited beast had landed midship, between Saul and the safety of the engine house. Its great bulk rested against the door, with its tail continually slamming against the wooden hull. The massive snout curled inward toward Saul, flashing a mouthful of huge jagged teeth. He was trapped. Saul bellowed to Charlie to get the axe, but his words seemed to bounce off the wind and echo back on him. Charlie could not hear him.

Saul edged his way along the port side. If he could reach the engine house, he could get the axe. Moving slowly, while dodging the rhythmic swing of the powerful tail fin, he crept closer and closer. He was about to make a dash for the door when he realized that the shark's massive body was positioned against the entrance. He couldn't get inside to get an axe.

The creature was so close now he could hear it gasping for air. He took a deep breath and then leapt over the dorsal fin and grabbed onto the upright on the edge of the engine house. His legs scraped against the rough skin of the brute as he crawled up the side and onto the roof.

It was then that Charlie noticed that Saul was standing on the roof. When Saul turned and looked down at his friend, Charlie knew that something was very wrong. He struggled to the roof, and before he could say anything, Saul pointed to the stern below.

Saul didn't have time to give his friend the details of the incident. Each time the frenzied animal slammed its great body against the deck, they felt the boat shudder and heard the crack of splintering wood. If the shark broke through, the *Miss Ruby* would surely sink.

Their only weapon was Charlie's filet knife, which was no match for such a beast. All they could do was watch as the shark exhausted its air supply and wore itself out. Although it was only a few minutes, it seemed like hours before the shark lay motionless on the deck below them. They believed it was dead, but they had to be sure. Charlie held his knife out like a sword while Saul gingerly crawled down to the engine house door. He managed to pry it open just enough so he could grab the axe. Without hesitation, they made certain of the shark's demise.

By the time they were ready to head for shore, they had overcome their shock and were joking about the incident. Saul took the wheel and set course for the tip of Manhattan, where they sold their five-hundred-pound monster at the Fulton Fish Market. Neither man was sure what folks did with shark, and they didn't care. It had been a great fishing trip, and the money they made from the shark was a real bonus.

CHAPTER 8

1941–1960

JULY 23, 1941

OFF BRIELLE, NJSAF #39

The summer of 1941 would be the last summer of peace for some years to come. Rumors of impending war had been growing for some time, and the talk on the street was of the European conflict, as it seemed only a matter of time before America joined in the fray.

As the Depression began to recede, recreational activities of all kinds began to prosper again. Although the Depression years had been difficult for Captain Lonergan and his charter fishing boat, business was improving this summer. Since mid-June, he had been able to book at least three tuna charters a week. It was almost like old times.

Captain Lonergan, like his father before him, ran fishing charters out of Brielle, New Jersey. For several years, he had specialized in sport fishing, especially tuna. By the early spring of 1941, his forty-eight-foot cruiser, *Bingo III*, was a fully equipped tuna boat complete with all the latest fishing gear, including quality saltwater reels, heavy-duty rods, tackle and premium lures and baits.

Although the *Bingo III* occasionally was chartered by local fishermen with experience fishing for the feisty tuna, that was not the usual clientele. Most of the patrons aboard the *Bingo III* were businessmen from nearby Philadelphia or New York City. They usually came in small groups and were often fishing

for tuna for the very first time. This required the captain to provide enough crew members to partner with the clients to provide them with instruction and assistance.

The charter for July 23 was booked three weeks in advance by two businessmen from the Philadelphia area. Normally, with only two clients, Lonergan would have brought along two crew members, but on this charter, he carried an extra deckhand. Captain Lonergan could tell by the questions they asked that they had little or no experience with deep-sea fishing. The deposit arrived promptly on schedule, and so as the sun was rising that morning, the *Bingo III* bobbed gently in the water, ready to receive its clients.

Both captain and crew were dressed casually in T-shirts and canvas pants for a day on the water. The boat was fully outfitted, and as they waited, the captain reminded the crew that the clients were novice fishermen and had likely never been on this sort of vessel before. He added that they would require a great deal of assistance.

It was then that they saw two men sauntering down the dock toward the *Bingo III*. Both men were in their thirties and quite well turned out for a fishing trip. The captain noticed that the taller man was dressed in a brightly colored Hawaiian shirt and color-coordinated linen trousers. The shorter of the two was wearing a pinstriped shirt with neatly pressed poplin slacks.

By the early 1940s, as the Depression dissipated, charter fishing boats once again became popular. *Courtesy of Pixabay.com.*

Each man had a sweater tied around his shoulders, and they were carrying wicker picnic hampers, a camera and a large canvas tote. The crew looked at one another and grinned. It was going to be an interesting day.

After he greeted the two men and introduced them to the crew, Captain Lonergan excused himself to prepare to disembark. The crew showed Michael and George around the boat and where to store their gear. Gerald, who was acting as first mate, suggested they get comfortable and that once they were underway, he would explain the plans for the day. The two guests dropped their bags and immediately opened their thermoses and stretched out in the sun to sip coffee as the *Bingo III* headed out of port.

As soon as land was out of sight, Gerald brought the clients to the stern, where he began to explain the workings of the *Bingo III* and the plans for the tuna fishing. The men listened intently, sometimes sharing a puzzled look or commenting, "Oh, really?"

Gerald was thorough. He explained that tuna fishing is a very specialized sport that requires patience as well as skill. Then he demonstrated the proper techniques of using the saltwater rods and reels and had each man practice casting and reeling in the line. Gerald repeated more than once the importance of keeping the pole pointed toward the fish and keeping the line taut, but not so tight as to break. He assured Michael and George that the crew would thread the hooks for them to ensure that the bait wasn't lost.

Finally, he gave each man a pair of thick gloves and asked them to put them on. He explained that without them, they would likely wear callouses into the palms of their hands while reeling in a fish. Michael and George held the gloves in their hands as he finished his "tuna lesson" with one admonishment: "Remember that fish you hook may be twenty pounds or it may be two hundred. You won't be able to tell at first. Landing a big fish is not easy. Don't be shy; we are here to help you land that trophy fish."

At last they reached the tuna grounds. While the crew was heaving buckets of chum into the water, Michael and George sat on deck chairs examining the heavy saltwater rods in their laps. They practiced closing and releasing the drag on the reel and then parleyed a friendly wager about who would catch the first fish.

Within minutes, the substantial amount of chum had spread several yards from the boat in all directions, forming a crimson ring around the *Bingo III*. The captain glanced over and saw his clients sunning themselves and chatting with the crew.

He was just about to give the order to cast lines when a large gray shark suddenly charged the boat. It vaulted into the air and landed smack on

Michael's lap. The force of the impact broke the rod in his hand and the chair collapsed, with Michael and the mako toppling onto the deck in a great heap.

George reached for his friend only to be slapped by the giant tail and knocked across the deck. The crew immediately yanked Michael away from the thrashing angry shark. He stood to the side, staring at the contorting creature as it hammered the deck and gnawed on the woodwork with great jagged teeth.

As the 158-pound mako flailed and squirmed, it tumbled into the narrow footway between the cabin and the gunwale. At last it was trapped. Confined in the narrow space, the shark finally expired.

Once they were assured that the shark was dead, the two clients began snapping pictures. They took photos of the carcass, of themselves with the dead shark and even a group picture of the captain and crew with the shark. Any concern the captain had that the clients were disappointed in their charter vanished as Michael and George gleefully talked about their wonderful catch.

Michael marveled that he never thought he would be able to catch such a huge shark. No one had the heart to tell him that technically, he didn't catch the shark; it was the shark that caught him. Nonetheless, the clients went home happy with their photos, and the crew went home pleased with their sizeable gratuities.

JULY 12, 1945

POINT PLEASANT, NJSAF #57

To describe 1945 merely as a historically eventful year would be a gross understatement. America was a war-weary nation as FDR began his fourth term. We were fighting on two fronts, both in Europe and the Pacific. Essential supplies like sugar, gasoline and meat were rationed; thousands of men were fighting overseas; and women were manning the factories and offices all around the nation. As casualties mounted, many struggled to remain optimistic and prayed for an end to the bloodshed.

In April, the president died unexpectedly, and in the following month, the Allies announced that Hitler was dead. May 8 was VE Day (Victory in Europe Day) and caused rejoicing across the western world. Although a

With the nation fighting a war on two fronts, America's fishing fleets struggled to help feed the civilian population. *Courtesy of the Library of Congress/Office of War Information.*

great weight had been taken from our shoulders, we could not forget that we were still embroiled in a war in the Pacific.

For most of that summer, the Jersey shore remained in war mode. Although the fear of German submarines was eliminated, there remained a huge humanitarian effort going on in Europe, not to mention the continued fighting in the Pacific. So it is not surprising that when a fishing boat from the Seashore Fishing Company of Point Pleasant headed out to sea on July 12, the mood remained in a "keep working" mode.

Some of the crew had been excused from military service due to the essential nature of their work, yet other fishermen enlisted. As a result, there were several new less experienced men among the crew this trip. Regardless, each man knew his job and the importance of bringing home a good catch.

With many commercial fishermen at the front, civilians were conscripted to acquire the skills essential for the nation's fishing fleets. *Courtesy of the Library of Congress/Office of War Information.*

They had been working for several hours when someone hooked a shark. Sometimes fishermen will cut the line when they catch such a beast, but this was wartime, and any fish considered edible was harvested. After what seemed like a lengthy battle, the men were able to yank the creature on board.

Not as feisty as it once was, the shark still refused to succumb. It thrashed this way and that, battering the side and deck of the boat with its great tail. Crewman Fred Hansen grabbed a piece of rope and fashioned a lasso and was attempting to snare the tail when it suddenly lashed at him, knocking him over the side into the water.

Other crewmen quickly took up the task of restraining the shark while a few others scurried to toss a line to Fred, who was treading water off the

port side. He quickly retrieved the rope and was hauled back on board, wet but uninjured.

There were no other injuries during the incident. The eleven-foot, 250-pound great white shark, the first such animal to be caught that year, was not so fortunate. After a struggle with the crew, the shark was summarily dispatched and taken to the Philadelphia Fish Market, where it was sold.

AUGUST 21, 1960

SEA GIRT, NJSAF #40

The summer of 1960 is remembered for an ongoing cold war that seemed to grow warmer each day. At the same time, a lively presidential election campaign was raging between Richard Nixon and young John Kennedy.

Rock-and-roll had already conquered America. Elvis was discharged from the army, and Chubby Checkers's dance craze the Twist had sock hops contorting all summer long. But best of all, color television was gaining in popularity and availability, with more and more shows being broadcast in "living color."

Despite the headlines, folks still flocked to the shore when vacation time came around. Some came for the entire season, while others booked for only a few weeks, a weekend or sometimes just a day. This influx of visitors created a wealth of temporary summer jobs in the local area. College students as well as local schoolteachers filled many of these positions in restaurants and hotels up and down the Jersey coast. One of these young teachers was twenty-two-year-old Jean Filoramo of Jersey City. She was spending the summer of 1960 working in a hotel in the exclusive community of Sea Girt. It was a pleasant upscale community in which to both work and spend the summer. The small town consisted of a limited but tasteful business district, numerous elegant stately homes and a few exclusive hotels.

Jean had been in Sea Girt since just after Memorial Day and would not be leaving until the day after Labor Day. She was thrilled when her parents and her fiancé, John Brodeur, arrived for a short visit that Sunday afternoon. With her duties completed for the day, she took the opportunity to take them to the hotel's employee beach area to enjoy the warm ocean waters and the late afternoon breeze.

SHARK ATTACKS OF THE JERSEY SHORE

It was after four o'clock when they finished their picnic. While her parents settled in their dune chairs, Jean and John headed to the water's edge. There had been a thunderstorm the day before, and the ocean was still rather furious. With the tide coming in, the white caps broke closer to the shore, and the waves seemed to swell just before they crashed on the beach.

The two ran into the water and immersed themselves in the next wave. They emerged laughing and continued chatting as they wandered farther away from shore. When they were twenty-five yards from the beach, Jean turned to wave to her parents. As the next breaker approached, John said he was going to ride the wave into shore.

Just as it was upon them, John shrieked, "I'm bitten!" Jean watched in horror as the water began to turn red around him. When John began to stagger toward the beach, Jean rushed to try and support his weight.

A lifeguard spied the fracas and rushed into the water and pulled John onto the beach. Bone protruded through the bloody mass of torn muscle and tissue as blood streamed down his leg onto the sand. According to witnesses, the lifeguard panicked. It was an ex-marine, Norman Porter, who raced to John's side. He tore off his belt and used it as a tourniquet to stop the profuse bleeding.

An ambulance arrived, and John was rushed to Fitkin Hospital (now known as Jersey Shore Medical Center) in Neptune. There, his extensive injuries were evaluated. He had a huge jagged laceration extending through his thigh as well as his calf on his right leg. The tibia and fibula were both exposed, as were the major blood vessels, some of which were severed. Muscle tissue was shredded, and a wedge of bone was completely missing.

He immediately was administered eight units of blood and underwent a four-hour emergency operation to return circulation to his right leg, but it was unsuccessful. Ten days later, the right leg was amputated. Based on the pattern of the bite marks, the culprit was identified as a twelve- to seventeen-foot-long sand tiger shark.

John Brodeur lived to be seventy-five years old, passing away in 2011. During the fifty-some years since the attack, he has been interviewed multiple times for books and appeared on television. A successful accountant, John led a full and rich life. He always spoke willingly about that fateful day. He described seeing what looked like a long dark telephone pole coming toward him in the water and then feeling the sudden jolt of pain as the creature bit him.

He recalled the panicked lifeguard and seeing blood everywhere. But most of all he remembered Norman Porter, a man he called his hero. It was Norman, the ex-marine, who sprang into action that day and saved his life.

He commented that he doesn't remember much pain that day, but he will always remember the man who saved his life. He and Norman remained friends until Norman passed away.

Although he walked with a prosthetic leg for the remainder of his life, John took it all in stride. He couldn't run, but he could walk. He was even known to play tennis. According to his family and friends, John simply never viewed the amputation as a handicap. He was too busy living life.

AUGUST 22, 1960

SEASIDE PARK, NJSAF #41

It was the third week of August in 1960, and the summer was winding down. Only a fortnight remained in the tourist season. Already some visitors were checking out, dragging their youngsters home to go shopping for school clothes. All too soon the beaches, the boardwalk and the local businesses would be empty once again. There would be little profit until next Memorial Day when the tourists arrived once more.

As word spread about the shark attack in Sea Girt the day before, the Seaside Park business community cringed in unison. The profits they made during these last two weeks in August were critical. It would be a long nine months before they once again began turning a profit. All they could do was put on smiling faces and hold their breath.

Monday, August 22, 1960, started out in good fashion. A cloudless sky, along with a gentle three-mile-an-hour breeze and the eighty-four-degree temperature, created a purely idyllic beach day. The beaches and boardwalks filled quickly, and business was brisk by noon.

Just after three o'clock, fourteen-year-old Thomas McDonald and his pals were swimming a few yards offshore. Suddenly, Thomas felt a sharp pain on his knee. He yelped in pain and raced from the water, shouting that he had been bitten by a shark. The beach emptied as he ran screaming and sobbing for his mother. Within minutes, news had spread up and down the Seaside boardwalk.

Thomas was seen by a local doctor, who cleaned the deep laceration to his knee. Despite Thomas's assertions that he had been bitten by a shark, the physician insisted that his injury was not a shark bite at all. He concluded that the boy had swum into some debris in the water.

As word spread and rumors began to fly, towns up and down the coast closed their beaches as a precaution. Shore communities as far north as Long Branch and as far south as Toms River restricted access to the beaches. A navy helicopter scanned the surf for signs of a shark.

By August 23, the media had picked up on the story. The *Red Bank Register* gave front-page coverage to both the Sea Girt attack as well as the reported attack in Seaside Park. The paper included the assertion from A. Heaton Underhill, the chief of the New Jersey State Fish and Game Division, that the injuries to John Brodeur in Sea Girt were not from a shark.

Happily, regardless of the cause, Thomas's injuries were not serious. We have no photos or any written medical notes from that date. Neither is there any documented testimony from the teenager. It is impossible to tell if this was the imagination of a fourteen-year-old, aroused by the reports of the shark attack the day before, or if indeed he was nipped by an inquisitive shark. Yet we must remember as well that it would not have been the first time that the business community and the media joined forces to shroud the news of local shark attacks.

So, was young Thomas McDonald bitten by a shark? Your guess is as good as mine.

AUGUST 30, 1960

OCEAN CITY, NJSAF #42

Tuesday, August 30, 1960, was a perfect beach day. There was a gentle breeze, the temperatures stayed in the high eighties and the ocean was a warm seventy-five degrees. With less than a week to go before Labor Day, the beaches along the Jersey shore were filled with people grasping for those last few days of sun and surf. The baseball season was waning, and it looked like the Pirates would be pitted against the Yankees in the World Series. The presidential election was said to be a dead heat.

Richard Chung, known to his friends as Rich, was a twenty-five-year-old medical student completing his training at a suburban Philadelphia hospital. In addition to excelling in his medical studies, he was also a gifted athlete. He frequently headed to nearby Ocean City on his day off to train for an upcoming long-distance swimming competition. He usually swam for about two and a half hours in the deeper waters about half a mile offshore. Today,

he was trying to increase his speed and complete the workout a bit early, as he had an appointment to meet a friend back on the beach.

Rich had just finished his training session and was resting in about thirty feet of water when he spied a circle of what he dubbed "boiling waters." The surface was teeming with baitfish that were hurtling this way and that, sometimes even becoming airborne to avoid larger fish.

He turned and began the swim back to the beach when he was struck full force on his right calf. If the impact didn't take his breath away, the sight of the huge shark attached to his leg surely did. Instinctively, he began hammering on the creature's snout with his fists. At that moment, something that felt like sandpaper brushed against his other leg. As he glanced up, he saw three dorsal fins slice through the surface near him.

With a great bellow, he thrust his body forward toward the shore. A police officer walking the boardwalk saw the disturbance and quickly alerted the lifeguards. Within minutes, the guards had launched the rescue boat.

By now, the water surrounding the swimmer was crimson with blood, and the guards feared the worst. As they approached, he cried out, "I've been bitten, bitten by a shark!" They promptly heaved him into the boat, where they examined the extent of his injuries. Tissue and muscle were torn away by a huge laceration that ripped deep into the bone of his right leg, allowing blood to gush from the appendage uncontrollably. One guard applied a tourniquet to halt the profuse bleeding, while the other rowed quickly to shore.

Richard Chung was rushed to Shore Memorial Hospital in Sommers Point, where he underwent emergency surgery for his injuries. Although the wounds penetrated bone and tore jagged hunks of muscle from his leg, the doctors did not identify it as a shark bite. They categorized the wound as "an injury from some sort of fish." It is safe to assume that Richard Chung, having such a strong background in biology, accurately identified the creature that attacked him, so his identification seems valid.

Dr. Chung recovered from his injuries. He went on to live a long and productive life not only as a physician but also remained a competitive long-distance swimmer for many years.

This third attack in the summer of 1960 would be the last for that summer season. It would be nearly two years before the cry of "Shark!" would once again echo across our beaches.

1962–2000

AUGUST 12, 1962

MANASQUAN, NJSAF #43

The year 1962 had been an auspicious one for America. Now in his second year as president, John Kennedy utilized television not only for political purposes but also as a tool to energize and inform the public. A new sense of pride arose in February when America successfully launched astronaut John Glenn into orbit around the Earth. The enthusiasm and pride only grew when President Kennedy announced in May that we would put a man on the moon in this century. Then only a few months later in July, our new communications satellite, Telstar, made it possible to transmit live broadcasts from America to Europe for the very first time. Kennedy appeared on the broadcast himself, highlighting our nation's achievements and sharing our goals of peace and prosperity.

As schools and colleges recessed for the summer, buoyant Americans loaded up the family car and took to the vast interstate highway system that crisscrossed the United States. For the first time, people were driving long distances as part of their vacations. This brought more people to the Jersey shore than ever before. Business was booming, and the beaches were full of happy vacationers.

The weekend of August 12 was one of the busiest of the summer season. Folks came from near and far to the small town of Manasquan, New Jersey,

to enjoy the local hospitality, great seafood and, of course, the immaculate beaches. The weather cooperated as well, with the temperatures rising into the high eighties all weekend.

One of those visitors enjoying the sun and surf was Michael Roman, a twenty-four-year-old United Parcel Post service representative from Queens, New York. Michael worked hard all week, putting in long hours, and was always happy to head for the shore for a weekend of sun and fun.

Michael and some friends had been in Manasquan since Friday night making the most of one of the final weekends of the summer. On Sunday, they met on the beach at First Avenue for an afternoon swim before heading back to New York. They dropped their towels on the beach and raced into the surf, laughing and calling out to one another.

They swam until they were fifty yards offshore. They were only in six to eight feet of water when Michael began swimming away from the group. He had not gone far before something rammed against his left thigh with ferocious force. The blow propelled him sideways, and he submerged for just a moment, taking in a mouthful of ocean water. He popped to the surface and glanced around. There was no pain, just a perceptible discomfort. In the next instant, however, he felt acute pain as sixteen razor-sharp teeth sank into his hand and arm. The creature held on for a minute and then disappeared into the depths.

As the water around him turned red, Michael began flailing about in a panic. An alert lifeguard, seeing the splashing, rushed to the victim and brought him to shore. Blood was gushing from his wounds, dripping off his left arm and streaming down his leg. The guard, Michael Curry, applied direct pressure to stem the flow of blood until the ambulance arrived.

The New Yorker was rushed to Point Pleasant hospital, where his wounds were treated. Doctors discovered a bloody semi-oval gash of seven to nine inches on his left thigh outlined by twenty individual punctures. The double row of teeth marks was an inch apart along the length of the laceration. His left hand and arm also suffered sixteen similar wounds that protruded even deeper into his flesh. Although physicians from the local shore hospital identified the bite as being from "an unknown fish," Dr. Paul Harner of the Marine Biology Lab at Island Beach State Park recognized the bite marks as those from a shark approximately six feet in length.

As had been the custom in recent years, many medical personnel chose not to attribute such injuries to a shark. Likewise, local media were not confident in characterizing them as shark attacks because it labeled local waters as "shark infested."

It is easy for an unsuspecting swimmer to be totally unaware that an apex predator is approaching. *Courtesy www.pixabay.com.*

Despite this tendency to deny the attacks, shore towns took instant action. Numerous beaches from Long Branch to Seaside Park were closed. Others created restricted bathing areas, using ropes to create smaller lifeguard zones. In addition, spotters were placed strategically along the beaches, boats patrolled the shoreline and the navy used helicopters to scan for sharks.

There were four reported shark sightings that weekend in the area, resulting in a definite reduction in the number of bathers that entire week. It was observed and publicized that an extremely large school of baitfish was migrating northward along the coastline that weekend, which may have enticed sharks to the area.

While hospitalized, Roman was interviewed and photographed by a local newspaper, where he admitted he didn't get a good look at the creature that attacked him. He recovered from his wounds and returned to UPS soon afterward. Although he remained very cautious in the water for many years to come, he never lost his love for the Jersey shore.

AUGUST 26, 1965

ATLANTIC CITY, NJSAF #44

The year 1965 marked the midway point in the decade known as the psychedelic '60s. The United States was mired down in Vietnam, civil rights marches echoed across the nation and American youth were planting ideas of non-conformity. Here along the Jersey shore, business was booming. The beaches were crowded with a new sort of summer visitor. In addition to the usual church groups and families, surfers came to spend the summer. Bikini-clad girls known as beach bunnies and surfer dudes in colorful baggies could be seen perched on tapered slices of fiberglass or polyurethane riding the ocean breakers as they swept ashore.

The surfing craze arose in California and Hawaii and quickly spread from the Pacific to the Atlantic. It brought a new lifestyle to the local shore, which included "surfer" music, movies, beach parties and even a new surfer jargon with words like "wipe out," "stoked" and "tubular" to the common lexicon.

The Jersey shore was not immune to the infectious music, athleticism and carefree beach lifestyle. If you couldn't surf yourself, you could relax on the beach listening to the music and watch the surfers ride the crests or be swallowed by breaking waves in spectacular wipeouts.

The summer was winding down that final week of August 1965. Both surfers and bathers made the most of every opportunity to swim, surf or just enjoy the warm sandy beach before the Labor Day weekend. The beaches along the coast were jammed that entire week. None was more crowded than those in Atlantic City. Its legendary boardwalk, famous Steel Pier and attractive free beaches brought people to the shore in droves.

One young guest, James Bloodworth, and his mother were vacationing that week in Atlantic City. They stayed in a rooming house near the boardwalk so James could spend most of his waking hours at the beach. He loved the outdoors and took every opportunity to improve his skills swimming in the Atlantic surf. When he wasn't swimming or trying to learn to surf, he could be found playing volleyball on the beach. That Thursday, August 26, was to be one of their last days in Atlantic City before returning home. It was a perfect beach day. The sky was cloudless, allowing the sun to push temperatures into the high eighties.

About five o'clock that afternoon, James headed up to the beach at Virginia Avenue for a leisurely swim. He entered the water not far from Steel Pier and swam alongside it for about 150 yards. He was a strong swimmer,

The shark is a powerful predator that can suddenly yank its victim beneath the surface before viciously crushing bones, shredding tissue and ripping away flesh with its razor-like teeth. *Courtesy www.pixabay.com.*

and as he often did, he swam past the breakers where most of the other bathers were congregated.

The water was a comfortable seventy degrees despite being somewhat murky from the recent humidity. James was floating with his eyes closed and his arms stretched wide when something grabbed his leg and yanked him into the depths. He opened his eyes while still under water and saw only a huge dark form attached to his leg. He wrenched away and, with his last bit of air, surged to the surface. As he pushed against the creature, his hands brushed the triangular dorsal fin of his attacker. When he emerged from the water, he choked in a deep breath and let out a blood-curdling scream.

Lifeguards heard the shrieks and rushed to deploy the rescue boat. As soon as they got James onboard, they took turns applying direct pressure to his wounds until they got to shore. There, they tightly wrapped his leg in towels, hoping to slow the bleeding. They rushed James to the State Street Aid Station. The head lifeguard took one look at the injured teen and called the police, who rushed the young man to the Atlantic City Hospital.

James's leg had multiple triangular gashes on the top, side and back of the knee area. The elongated laceration extended from his knee to his upper right thigh. After treatment to stop the bleeding, the teenager received over two hundred stitches to close the wound. He was released later that evening.

The Labor Day holiday was only a week away, and every effort was made to suppress news of the attack. Both the police and the hospital downplayed the incident even though the teenager had such serious injuries. The official report from the hospital cited James's wounds as "superficial lacerations, possibly from a shark."

James returned home to New York soon afterward. It is believed he recovered fully from what he described as an attack by a "large gray shark with a huge mouth."

News of the incident was not widely reported by local newspapers; rather, it would be the *Philadelphia Inquirer* that would release details of the "minor" incident in Atlantic City.

JUNE 22, 1966

REEDS BAY, BRIGANTINE, NJSAF #45

Coastal New Jersey is known for a wide variety of ocean fronts. Many people think only of the wide sandy beaches where boardwalks, amusement parks,

arcades and water slides dot the shoreline. Yet the 141 miles of New Jersey seashore also include commercial ports, barrier islands, small seaside towns and several protected wetlands and wildlife sanctuaries.

Just north of Atlantic City, along the eastern shore, dozens of small salt marsh islands and tidal mudflats dot the intercoastal waterway between the mainland and Brigantine, a six-mile barrier island on the west. Now part of the expanded Edwin Forsythe National Wildlife Refuge, these fifty thousand acres of protected wetlands are a haven to numerous marine and bird species. The refuge attracts not only shore and wading birds but also more than three hundred other species of migratory birds each year. Its natural beauty is cherished by nature lovers, bird watchers and the nearby locals who call it home.

On Wednesday, June 22, fifteen-year-old Harry Hiksdal and a friend were clamming about one hundred feet offshore in Reeds Bay. It was a warm sunny day with temperatures in the low eighties. According to reports, one of the boys speared what they called a big fish. They were headed to shore, dragging the skewered creature behind them, when Harry's leg came too close to the wounded animal. It sunk its teeth deep into his flesh, leaving three bloody slashes on his right leg. Although the wounds were bleeding profusely, his friend managed to get him to Fisherman's Wharf on Brigantine Avenue, where an ambulance rushed Harry to Atlantic City Hospital for treatment.

Authorities did not identify the species of shark responsible for the injuries. Although experts insisted that the sixty-degree water temperature was too cold for sharks, the next day a fisherman caught a six-foot, two-hundred-pound sandbar shark nearby. Harry recovered from his injuries, earning bragging rights that he had been bitten by a shark and survived.

OCTOBER 21, 1975

SANDY HOOK, NJSAF #46

At the northern end of the New Jersey shoreline lies a unique and beautiful sand pit peninsula known to locals as "the Hook," or to others as Sandy Hook. Officially known as Gate Way National Park, this popular tourist spot welcomes over two million visitors each year. Although it varies in width from a tenth of a mile to just over a mile in some spots, Sandy

Hook's beautiful wide beaches and natural beauty draw not only beach lovers but also nature enthusiasts, sport fishermen, avid hikers, bikers and lovers of history to its shores.

The six-mile-long "Hook" encloses the southern end of New York harbor, resulting in an expansive bay that is convenient for ship anchorage as well as countless recreational activities. On the eastern shore, wide sandy beaches run the length of the park from the entrance to the very tip of the hook. A maritime holly forest, sand dune trails, seven bathing and fishing beaches and even a clothing-optional beach make it a delight for tourists. In addition, visitors will find a U.S. Coast Guard station, Historic Fort Hancock, the National Oceanic Atmospheric Administration Marine Science Laboratory and MAST (the Marine Academy of Science and Technology) High School.

The history of Sandy Hook is both rich and colorful. It has been a strategic military site since colonial times. The location was so critical to commerce that a lighthouse, which still stands today, was erected in 1764. During the American Revolution, the British captured Sandy Hook and held it until 1783. It was their base of operations throughout the entire war. The tiny sand spit would play important roles in every military action since. Even during the Cold War, Nike missile batteries housed here were part of America's strategic defense.

Surf fishing has been popular for decades; only the fishermen's attire seems to have changed. *Courtesy of the Library of Congress.*

Although most people visit the park during the summer, many others find the off-season their favorite time to visit. Fishermen find Sandy Hook especially appealing with its calm bay waters on the west and the energetic Atlantic Ocean surf on the east. Regardless of the time of year, or even the weather, you will likely find fishermen on Sandy Hook.

Such was the case on October 21, 1975. It was a typical October day. Although the masses of tourists had been gone since Labor Day, the park still welcomed visitors to enjoy the cool autumn beach. The air temperature that day was a breezy fifty-five degrees, far too cold for swimming but perfect for fishermen such as Vincent Limongelli. Mid-morning found the forty-one-year-old Elberon man surf fishing on the oceanside of the Hook just south of what is today Beach A. Like many fishermen, he wore rubber hip waders to keep his feet dry as he waded into the chilly surf to cast his line into the breaking waves. It isn't known what he was hoping to catch that day, although some reports hypothesize that it was likely bluefish.

Vincent waded into the surf with his rod in hand. As he looked across the surface of the water, he saw an immense splash. Just then, something grabbed him and pulled him into the water. He managed to escape the hold of the unseen creature and make it back to the beach.

There, he discovered something had bitten through his rubber wader boot and had lacerated his right calf. Park rangers rushed him to the Spermaceti Visitor Center's first aid station. When his wound was inspected more closely, he was immediately transported to Riverview Hospital in Red Bank for treatment. The hospital indicated the wound was likely a shark bite. The seven-inch puncture tear on his calf was treated and sutured before he was released.

As a precaution, the park rangers ordered visitors in the park to stay out of the surf. His boots and photos of the injuries were sent to the Sandy Hook Marine Lab for further investigation. Scientists found the attack to be an anomaly, as the water temperature was a chilly fifty-nine degrees, not popular with most sharks.

There were no reports that Vincent suffered any further difficulties as a result of the attack. Hopefully he soon resumed fishing in the beautiful surf of Sandy Hook.

JULY 27, 1980

OCEAN CITY, NJSAF #47

The summer heat wave of 1980 would be remembered as one of the worst in modern times. The prolonged intense heat and humidity that savaged more than twenty U.S. states spared the Jersey coast most of its wrath. While millions across the nation suffered drought, power losses and agricultural failures, our shores were fortunate to enjoy relatively mild summer temperatures averaging in the mid-eighties. In fact, it was by most accounts nearly a perfect summer season here on the New Jersey seaboard.

In Ocean City, New Jersey, located twenty miles south of Atlantic City and thirty miles north of Cape May, business was booming. The barrier island beach resort had been gaining popularity as a family-oriented vacation spot since its inception in 1879. Ocean City maintained its status as an alcohol-free vacation destination that catered to families with wholesome recreational activities. In addition to its eight miles of sandy beaches, the two-and-a-half-mile immaculate boardwalk featured well-kept hotels, gift stores, amusements and a variety of family restaurants and ice cream and fudge shops.

This is what brought the Mofatt family from Hatboro, Pennsylvania, to the Jersey shore that final week in June 1980. The parents and their two sons, ages thirteen and fourteen, had planned the two-week vacation in Ocean City earlier that spring and were happy to be on the beach at last.

The weather took a turn for the worse that Friday. By noon, the sun was obscured by an expanding layer of thick dark clouds. The brisk wind of early morning was brewing into a storm. The waves were growing in intensity, and the turbidity had turned the water a murky gray.

Despite this, the air temperature remained in the mid-eighties, and the water was a comfortable seventy degrees. For many vacationers, it was simply not an ideal day for the beach. But to the Mofatt brothers, who loved to body surf on the incoming breakers, it was a perfect day.

Midafternoon found the Fourteenth Street beach nearly deserted. The few visitors who remained began packing up and leaving by two o'clock as the storm clouds moved in closer, leaving only a few swimmers, a fisherman on a nearby pier and the two teenagers body surfing on the frothy breakers.

It was high tide, and the waves seemed to be growing larger. They had been surfing for about thirty minutes and had swam out about seventy-five feet from the shore where the waves were beginning to break. There they

Although surfers respect the "man in the gray suit," any sighting of a shark is cause for alarm. *Courtesy of www.pixabay.com.*

waited for just the right moment before propelling themselves into the crest and riding it to shore. Jeff, the older six-foot, 150-pound brother, caught the next wave. As he catapulted through the water, he was attempting a somersault maneuver when his back struck something in the water. It was hard and felt like he had rammed an underwater rock.

It wasn't until the two reached the shore that his younger brother saw the injury on Jeff's back. When they showed the wound to the lifeguard, he immediately began blowing his whistle and calling everyone out of the water. The teens were taken to the Twelfth Street Aid Station, where the bloody injury received closer inspection. Soon after his parents arrived, Jeff was transported to Shore Memorial Hospital in Somers Point.

The teen received sixty stitches to close the semicircular puncture wounds to the small of his back. Treated as an outpatient, he was instructed to go back into the ocean as soon as the stitches were removed, as the saltwater would aid in healing.

Not only was the species of shark never identified, but there were some who claimed that the teen was not bitten by a shark at all. They insisted that he likely struck some debris in the water during his somersault. One guard who first stated he had seen a fin in the water at the time contends that the beach patrol captain told him to keep quiet.

As is often the case when shark attacks occur in popular tourist areas, the events of the day were not publicized. Since then, a former lifeguard from Ocean City, now a successful businessman, quipped, "A shark could walk up the boardwalk and order a hamburger and everyone would say they didn't see it."

Photos were taken of the wound only after suturing, yet the punctures and razor-like lacerations are persuasive evidence that Jeff Mofatt did indeed collide with a shark.

2005–2014

JUNE 5, 2005

SURF CITY, LONG BEACH ISLAND, NJSAF #48

Although the Jersey shore usually shivers in sub-freezing temperatures as the New Year begins, 2005 would begin much differently. Temperatures had remained mild ever since the holiday season, and now on the first day of January, temperatures ranged in the high forties and low fifties. The respite from the cold continued well into February.

That very same month in suburban California, a soon-to-be Internet giant was born. Within months, YouTube was a household word. The three young co-founders would sell their business only a year and a half later for $1.6 billion.

By the time Memorial Day rolled around, everyone had certainly ditched their outerwear and was focused on the coming summer season. Up and down the shore, beaches were prepared, shops restocked and restaurants revamped as shore towns began receiving reservations for the summer season.

Such was the case in Surf City, on Long Beach Island, where large and small businesses alike geared up for the first holiday weekend of the summer. They were not disappointed. Memorial Day weekend brought thousands to the beaches. "No Vacancy" signs appeared at local lodgings, restaurants were filled and shopkeepers were happy to once more hear the jingle of the cash register.

June 5 was the first Sunday of the month, and the day could not have been more perfect. The sun darted in and out of clouds, keeping the air temperature a balmy eighty-six degrees. All along Surf City's Boulevard district, business was brisk. Day-trippers and vacationers alike crowded the local beaches to enjoy these first days of summer. Despite the somewhat nippy fifty-degree water temperatures, thousands took their first plunges of the summer into the chilly waters of the Atlantic.

Ryan Holton, a seventeen-year-old surfing enthusiast from nearby Forked River, was spending the day on the Eighteenth Avenue beach with his family and his beloved surfboard. Ryan was making the most of his day at the beach. By eleven o'clock he was seen surfing the waters along the fishing jetty some fifteen feet seaward of the sandbar. He paddled out past the breakers and waited for a wave. At just the right moment, he mounted his board and, crouching slightly, rode the surf into shore.

Around 11:30 a.m., Ryan paddled just beyond the breakers. He caught the next wave and rode it safely to the shore. As he leapt from the board into about three feet of water, he felt a sharp blow to his right ankle. Not sure at the time what had hit him, he made his way to the beach, propelling himself forward with one foot. Lifeguards and bystanders saw the bloody three-inch semicircular laceration across his right ankle and called for help.

Within moments, his family came to his side. Ryan was rushed to Southern Ocean County Hospital, where fifty stitches were required to close the wound. At the time, the emergency room physician concurred that it was likely a shark bite.

The family took photos of the wound and sent them to shark expert George Burgess, director of the International Shark Attack File and shark expert for the Florida Museum of Natural History. From the photos, Burgess identified the bite as that from a six-foot great white shark, likely two to three years old. He documented definite impressions on the skin, citing that it was certainly a shark bite.

The Holton family notified the press, and soon both local and national media were reporting news of the attack in Surf City. The entire Jersey shore was abuzz. *Eyewitness News*, from a New York television station, interviewed the victim. When quizzed, the teenager was quite matter-of-fact about the incident, saying, "It felt like a baseball bat that came and whacked my foot, and then I looked over and there was a huge chunk missing."

According to some sources, business remained brisk and the vacationers were back in the water the following day. One pizzeria even advertised a

The media doesn't hesitate to sensationalize any shark sighting or encounter. *Courtesy of www.pixabay.com.*

special "great white pizza." Others reported that significant damage was done to the local economy as word of the attack spread.

The local police, however, did not record the incident as a shark attack. Almost immediately, a controversy arose about the legitimacy of the claim. Other shark specialists such as Ralph Collier, author of *Shark Attacks of the 20th Century*, and Dr. Erich Ritter, author and shark attack file expert, were quick to disagree with the Burgess identification. Also entering the fray was Marie Levine-Global, an author and archivist for Global Shark Attack File, who could not see definite tooth marks. They concluded that the injury was more likely from underwater debris.

Some of the media began to question the legitimacy of the claim, reporting that a witness in the emergency room at the time claimed that Ryan himself commented that he had been struck on his ankle by his surfboard. Several media outlets concurred that the teen never claimed to have seen a shark at all.

When the controversy had not subsided by the end of the week, two marine biologists from the Shark Research Institute carried out an underwater survey of the scene. Their search revealed a large amount of underwater debris in the area, including timbers, rocks, pipes and garbage.

The local authorities failed to identify the incident as a shark attack, although such an event occurring was a definite possibility. Several species of sharks, including great whites, are frequent visitors to the Jersey shore during the summer season. Happily, Ryan Holton recovered from his injuries after spending some time on crutches and missing out on most of the surfing that summer.

DECEMBER 6, 2009

CAMDEN, NJSAF #49

Sunday, December 6, 2009, is remembered as a blustery and rain-swept day along coastal New Jersey. With temperatures in the upper thirties for most of the day, the shore was hammered by downpours that lasted until midafternoon. By evening, a cold front had moved in and snow began to fall all along the coast. Some areas received only an inch or two, while others received up to five inches.

In Camden, located on the Delaware River across from Philadelphia, it was business as usual at the Adventure Aquarium. The popular tourist attraction and teaching center had been in this location since 1992. Although once maintained by the State of New Jersey, the aquarium was now part of the New Jersey Academy of Aquatic Sciences. Major renovations over the years resulted in a large modern complex with two million gallons of aquaria housing over eight thousand specimens. Aquatic animals from wetlands, lakes, rivers and the ocean were on display. One of the most popular attractions was the large collection of sharks, known as Shark Realm.

On December 6, two volunteer divers for the academy entered the massive shark tank for regular scheduled maintenance. Both fifty-seven-year-old Robert Large and his teammate, Ed Frankel, were veteran divers. Both had experience working in the fifteen-foot tank and were familiar with its numerous predatory inhabitants.

It was about one o'clock in the afternoon when the two entered the shark tank wearing complete scuba gear, including full Farmer John black wet suits. The water in the aquarium was maintained at sixty-five degrees Fahrenheit and was crystal clear.

Robert entered the tank by stepping backward down the metal ladder, rung by rung, until his feet and legs were submerged. As he moved away from the final step, he bumped into something directly behind him in the water. At the same instant, something grabbed hold of his calf. He claimed later that although it didn't hurt, it felt as if his leg was being held in a vice. For a moment, he thought it was a turtle.

Then he looked around and saw a seven-foot sand tiger shark with a firm grip on his leg. He pulled his leg closer to his body, thinking the shark would release him, but to no avail. It wasn't until he twisted his body nearly 180 degrees that the shark let go and quickly disappeared.

His dive partner, who was four feet away, watched as the sand tiger swam away from the injured diver. Robert was able to quickly ascend the ladder and escape the tank. Ed administered first aid as they awaited the arrival of the ambulance. Robert was taken to Cooper University Hospital, where he underwent surgery for fifteen punctures and lacerations to the lower calf, ankle and foot. In addition, 25 percent of his Achilles tendon was damaged.

Although Robert was initially released after two days, he would be forced to return to the hospital soon afterward. The infected wound was X-rayed, revealing a fragment of shark tooth imbedded in the wound that had not been found during the previous surgery. After a second operation, Robert was hospitalized for an additional five days.

The seven-foot sand tiger shark in question, despite its ominous appearance and rows of sharp ragged teeth, was basically harmless. The several-hundred-pound specimen had been in captivity for some time and was well acclimated to its environment, as well as to the divers who frequented the tank.

Sand tigers are the most common sharks kept on display due to their tolerance for captivity and their placid nature. In the wild, these sharks are found all along our shorelines and offer no real threat to humans.

It would be a stretch to designate this as a shark attack. George Burgess, director of the International Shark Attack File, considered it a workplace incident rather than an attack. Technically, it was a provoked attack, as it involved a captive shark and the shark did not approach the diver. Rather, it was the diver who inadvertently bumped into the shark.

Robert Large recovered from the injury, and the sand tiger remained on display in the Shark Realm exhibit.

JULY 25, 2011

EGG HARBOR, NJSAF #50

The year 2011 is remembered for a wide variety of reasons. At first, it was the news that international hackers had accessed secure government and military Internet sites that made folks sit up and take notice in the early days of the new year. Then in mid-March, a catastrophic 9.1 earthquake rocked Japan. The resulting tsunami obliterated entire communities, killed

thousands and even threatened a catastrophic disaster by rupturing a major nuclear reactor.

In April, people worldwide took a breather as the future king of England married a commoner in an elaborate ceremony in London. Then in mid-May, President Obama announced the news that Americans had waited for since 2001: Osama Bin Laden had finally been captured and killed. It had been a remarkable beginning to the new year.

Two weeks later, the Memorial Day holiday ushered in the summer season along the Jersey shore. The region was bustling with both day-trippers and tourists racing to the beaches to find the primo spots on the sand. Local businesses geared up for the influx of visitors, everyone yearning for a lucrative summer season.

Of course, not all the people headed to the beaches were sunbathers, nor were they all tourists. Locals, too, began their summer routines, swimming, surfing and fishing at their favorite spots all along the coast.

Here along the Jersey shore, saltwater sport fishing is a major industry as well as a common pastime of local fishing enthusiasts. Deep-sea fishing requires boats and expensive tackle and gear. So it is not surprising that many locals prefer to fish from the beach. These surf fishermen are found the length of New Jersey's coastline as well as throughout the many bays, harbors and inlets. Although we usually spot them during the day, many surf fishermen prefer to fish the surf at night due to the nocturnal feeding habits of their prey. This enthusiastic group of sportsmen wade into the surf with their twelve- to fifteen-foot rods, casting as far as they can into the water. They are looking to hook a fluke, a bluefish, a whiting or, if they are lucky, a striped bass. It can be a dangerous sport, as there are often undertows, rough seas and sometimes even sharks patrolling these shallow waters.

Although you may see people fishing on the beach wearing shorts and going barefoot, most serious fishermen wear waterproof chest-high waders, wading belts cinched tightly around their waist to prevent water from entering their waders in the event of an accident. This indispensable gear for the surf fisherman protects him from the pounding surf, cold temperatures and injuries from rocks or debris found on the bottom.

July 25 was a classic summer day at the beach. The temperature rose to nearly ninety, with the sun shining brightly through a cloudless sky. Temperatures began to fall as dusk approached, and by nightfall, it was a cool sixty-seven degrees along the shores of Egg Harbor.

It was dark when two local fishermen, Eric Aubrey and Ryan Sherwood, reached the bay and headed into the surf in search of striped bass. They

wore neoprene waders as they ambled into waist-high water. As they were casting into the dark bay, Aubrey felt a strong tug at his left leg. He quickly jerked his leg back in response.

As they exited the surf, they saw the teeth marks on the left leg of Aubrey's waders. While no animal was seen, the two fishermen speculated that it might have been a sand tiger or a sandbar shark.

Although the Philadelphia NBC affiliate reported the incident as "Man's Waders Save Him from Shark Bite," there were no injuries from the possible shark encounter.

NOVEMBER 7, 2013

BAY HEAD, NJSAF #51

Much of 2013 was filled with an uneasiness that drifted around the globe like a wearisome cloud. It seemed that regardless of where you lived, the daily news was disproportionately filled with broadcasts that left us feeling concerned, apprehensive and sometimes even fearful. All too often, it was the account of yet another bombing in some crowded public place where lives were snuffed out and hundreds injured or maimed. At first it was in faraway places like Damascus, Baghdad or Pakistan. But then in April it came home to us when the Boston Marathon was shattered by a terrorists' bombing that killed three and injured almost three hundred. Then there was the seemingly endless stream of natural disasters around the globe, a meteor impact, hurricanes, floods, fires and even a tornado that obliterated a small Midwest town.

Of course, there was good news. The economy was stable and showing improvement, there were advancements in the treatment of cancer and Cornell University began using a 3D printer to make prosthetic human ears. We rushed to buy the new Sony PlayStations and Microsoft Xboxes in droves and to stand in long lines to purchase Apple's new 5C and 5S iPhone. People gossiped about storing their data on something called a cloud.

That first week of November was mild, with temperatures hovering in the mid-fifties. In Bay Head, New Jersey, a small residential community sandwiched along the shore between Point Pleasant Beach and Mantoloking, the town was bustling a bit more than usual for November. The public schools were closed that Thursday and Friday for the yearly teachers'

convention, so although youngsters could be seen scampering about town enjoying their break, it was business as usual for most of the residents.

Thursday, November 7, was a rather dreary day. Although the temperature was nearly fifty degrees in the morning, it began to drop as the day progressed. By midafternoon, it was a chilly forty-five degrees with a nippy fourteen-mile-an-hour breeze.

Although the thermometers were sinking that afternoon, it didn't deter the two body boarders who were anxious to take advantage of the school recess and the mild conditions to extend their surfing season as much as possible.

Midafternoon found the two sixteen-year-olds, Quinn Gates and a friend, body boarding just south of the Mount Street Jetty in Bay Head. They were observed by George Nicholas, a local geologist, who noted that the tight waves were giving the boys a good ride.

For an undisclosed reason, Quinn was wearing a light blue swim fin on his right foot and a black one on his left. The two were catching waves when Quinn felt a heavy pull on his right swim fin. He later reported, "I felt a tug on my fin; it was hanging on."

The Jersey shore is frequently visited by twenty different species of sharks, with another one hundred species occasional visitors. *Courtesy of www.pixabay.com.*

Although he managed to get out of the water quickly, all he could see was that a large chunk had been taken off the edge of the mangled blue silicone swim fin. Quinn was uninjured during the incident, although he later recalled, "It could have gotten my toes or feet." Some say the bite to the swim fin was from a six- to eight-foot shark. Other experts suggested that the blue fin might have been mistaken by the shark as some sort of prey.

Captain Stephen Nagiewicz, expert from the Shark Research Institute, reported that he was not particularly surprised by the event. He went on to explain that local waters are filled with many kinds of microorganisms that are a food source for small fish. Larger predators follow these schools, often coming close to our local beaches. Here in New Jersey, it is possible to spot whites, tigers, sand tigers and even an occasional bull shark near our shores.

Quinn Gates's Facebook page was filled with pictures of waves and body surfing. The teen remained optimistic and insisted he would not be deterred from the ocean, adding, "I will just have to pay attention more."

JUNE 21, 2014

OFF CAPE MAY, NJSAF #52

Located along the southernmost region of the New Jersey peninsula, Cape May has been a seaside resort since the mid-eighteenth century, when it began hosting vacationers from Philadelphia. It still retains its quiet Victorian charm, stunning scenery and historical architecture. For the adventuresome, there are beautiful beaches, water sports and prize-winning sport fishing opportunities.

It was the chance to do some deep-sea fishing that brought an engaged couple and their friend from Pennsylvania to Cape May on June 21, 2014. Courtney Stacherski and her fiancé, John CinQue, along with Steve Clark headed out to sea from Avalon, New Jersey, earlier that day for a bit of fishing.

The balmy sixty-nine-degree temperature and partly sunny skies made that Saturday a perfect day to be cruising out into deeper water. The fishing boat set course for an area about thirty miles offshore known to both scuba divers and fishermen as the "twenty-eight-mile wreck." It is the site of the wreckage of the Norwegian freighter the *Varanger*, which was torpedoed

The fearsome great white—aggressive, unpredictable, yet a wonder to be spotted in the wild. *Courtesy of www.pixabay.com.*

and sunk by a German U-boat in 1942. Since that time, scuba divers have extensively explored the wreckage of the upright freighter. It is equally popular with fishermen, as it is a congregating spot for giant blues, cod, bonito, skipjack and sharks, as well as the occasional marlin.

The trio was anchored near the wreck, enjoying the beautiful day, when a huge great white shark began circling their craft. At one point, the shark swam under the boat so that its head could be seen on the port and its tail on the starboard. They estimated the shark to be sixteen feet long and weigh between 1,200 and 1,400 pounds. Excited to see the sea creature in the wild, they watched it with amazement for about twenty minutes as it swam closer and closer to their boat.

Suddenly, as it passed alongside, it brought its huge head out of the water and attacked their chum bag, ravaging it with its huge mouth full of jagged teeth. Those on board were able to distinctly see its white underbelly and mottled grayish body. Fortunately, CinQue was filming and caught the entire event.

When the shark began attacking the propeller of their boat, they decided it was time to leave. They made their way back to Avalon unharmed. Likewise, the great white went on its way as well.

Later, Stacherski was interviewed on television, describing the incident as exciting and memorable. She reiterated that she was not afraid to go back out on the water and would do it again in a minute. Meanwhile, her fiancé's video went viral on the Internet, and the young couple were besieged with messages from around the world.

JUNE 11, 2013

THIRTY MILES EAST OF MANASQUAN INLET, NJSAF #53

Although sport fishing is considered a recreational activity, marine fishermen take their sport and their competitions seriously. One of the most popular among marine anglers is shark tournaments. They are held all along the Eastern Seaboard throughout the summer season, often drawing large crowds to their seaside weigh-ins.

Most tournaments are strictly regulated, with entries limited to one or two specific species. There are policies about minimum sizes, method of fishing and catch and release for bycatch. Even the number of crew permitted on each participating boat is regulated. Anyone caught cheating at an event will be blackballed from tournaments all along the coast.

There is often a hefty entrance fee for participation, so participants frequently prepare in advance for a tournament, scouting the local waters to choose the best spot from which to compete.

Such was the case on June 11, 2013, when Captain Tom Rostron of Wall, New Jersey, and his friend Clint Simek of Brielle were scouting areas off the Manasquan Inlet in preparation for an upcoming mako shark tournament. The two avid fishermen were aboard Rostron's thirty-one-foot boat, the *TNT*, about thirty miles offshore. Fishing had been good; they had already caught and released several blue sharks. With only a two-man crew, they had no intention of landing a large shark that day.

Earlier, there had been six-foot swells in the area, but by midafternoon, the winds had died down. The temperature was a balmy seventy-nine degrees, and the ocean was flat with no drift at all.

About 3:30 p.m., a mako shark began circling their boat, attacking their bait floats at random. As the circling continued, they tried baiting the fish. They began reeling in the deeper rods only to discover that the shark had taken the hook. Captain Rostron reported that the moment the hook was set, the mako shark shot fifteen feet into the air. These sharks are known to be jumpers, and

this one was no exception. As they continued to reel in the giant fish, it jumped three more times, each time falling back into the water with a great splash.

The beast circled under the boat and once again leapt from the water, flipping backward onto the bow of the boat. Landing with a thud, it instantly began thrashing about, attacking anything within reach. It slammed its great body this way and that, slashing its giant tail in every direction. At the same time, rows of sharp, jagged teeth chomped apart two broomsticks, shredded seat cushions and gnawed on a speaker before trying to pulverize the side of the boat.

The men stood back for a while, waiting in vain for the creature to tire. Then, as they struggled to control the shark, it swiped Clint with its great tail. During the prolonged struggle, Rostron gaffed the creature, and they were finally able to tie and wedge it to the side of the boat. With the eight-foot, three-hundred-pound carcass restrained, they headed for shore. There were no serious injuries from the incident, and Captain Rostron describes the experience as "amazing." He is certain it was a once-in-a-lifetime event.

JULY 27, 2017

VENTNOR, NJSAF #59

Although Ventnor, New Jersey, lies adjacent to Atlantic City and shares a popular wooden boardwalk, the small town features a less hectic beachfront and a quiet, more residential vibe. Locals and tourists alike praise the wide sandy beaches and family atmosphere. Many insist that Ventnor is the best-kept secret of the Jersey shore. So it isn't surprising that the newspapers of the day did not cover the encounter between Isabella Smith and a sand tiger shark. Although it was reported by the Global Shark Attack File, little is known except that she received an injury to her hand as a result of her interaction with the two-foot shark.

MAY 20, 2019

SHIP BOTTOM, NJSAF #60

Paul Sykes, a sixty-seven-year-old former lifeguard, was body boarding just off the Eighth Avenue beach in Ship Bottom. With both sunny skies and

temperatures in the high eighties, he had paddled out eighty to one hundred yards from shore and was resting on his board, waiting for a wave. Suddenly, something whacked him with such force he was nearly tossed into the water. He grabbed onto the board and looked up just in time to see the telltale fin. An experienced surfer and ocean guard, he immediately began to paddle until he caught a wave and rode it to shore and safety. Though struck on his left hip by the great beast, he had not been bitten. Paul reported his encounter to the Global Shark Attack File, which concurred that the culprit was likely a sand tiger. Since this species does not usually bite humans, it was probably chasing migrating baitfish along the shoreline.

THE NEW JERSEY SHARK ATTACK FILE

BY ROBERT J. HEYER

The New Jersey Shark Attack File was established in 1998 to investigate all possible incidents of shark attack within the waters of New Jersey. The current area of study are all the coastal waters of New Jersey, including rivers, bays and estuaries. Also included are freshwater bodies of water and aquariums.

The purpose of the file is to place all available data on shark attacks in one useful form to aid in the prevention of future incidents. When possible, the species of the shark involved will be determined. All known details of the incident, along with primary sources for the information, are included.

The New Jersey Shark Attack File shares its information with other scientific organizations, including the International Shark Attack File and Global Shark Attack File.

NJ001: July 6, 1842, Absecon
NJ002: August 28, 1884, Bayonne
NJ003: August 1886, Highlands
NJ004: August 1886, Sandy Hook
NJ005: August 1886, Highlands
NJ006: August 17, 1890, Sea Bright
NJ007: August 29, 1891, Longport
NJ008: August 2, 1895, Raritan Bay
NJ009: July 6, 1902, Atlantic City
NJ010: September 16, 1903, Atlantic City
NJ011: July 28, 1904, Navesink River (North Shrewsbury)
NJ012: August 1905, Atlantic City
NJ013: August 5, 1907, Delaware Bay
NJ014: August 27, 1913, Spring Lake
NJ015: August 27, 1913, Lavallette
NJ016: June 30, 1916, Atlantic City

NJ017: July 1, 1916, Beach Haven

NJ018: July 6, 1916, Spring Lake

NJ019: July 12, 1916, Matawan

NJ020: July 12, 1916, Matawan

NJ021: July 12, 1916, Matawan

NJ022: July 12, 1916, Matawan

NJ023: September 21, 1917, Sea Bright

NJ024: January 1, 1923, Ocean City

NJ025: January 1, 1923, Ocean City

NJ026: January 1, 1923, Sea Bright

NJ027: July 12, 1926, Sea Bright

NJ028: August 24, 1926, Seaside

NJ029: August 24, 1928, Offshore New Jersey

NJ030: November 18, 1928, Sea Bright

NJ031: July 15, 1931, Sea Girt

NJ032: August 6, 1931, Sandy Hook

NJ033: August 27, 1931, Navesink

NJ034: June 26, 1932, Ocean City

NJ035: June 28, 1932, Sea Isle City

NJ036: August 10, 1932, Mantoloking

NJ037: June 18, 1935, Offshore New Jersey

NJ038: June 12, 1936, Long Branch

NJ039: July 22, 1941, Brielle

NJ040: August 21, 1960, Sea Girt

NJ041: August 22, 1960, Seaside Park

NJ042: August 30, 1960, Ocean City

NJ043: August 12, 1962, Manasquan

NJ044: August 26, 1965, Atlantic City

NJ045: June 22, 1966, Brigantine

NJ046: October 21, 1975, Sandy Hook

NJ047: July 27, 1980, Ocean City

NJ048: June 5, 2005, Surf City

NJ049: December 5, 2009, Camden

NJ050: July 25, 2011, Egg Harbor

NJ051: November 7, 2013, Bay Head

NJ052: June 21, 2014, Cape May

NJ053: June 2014, Manasquan

NJ054: June 17, 1880, Sea Bright

NJ055: June 11, 1880, Sea Bright

NJ056: July 27, 1898, Long Branch

NJ057: July 12, 1945, Point Pleasant

NJ058: July 13, 1916, Sea Bright

NJ059: July 23, 2017, Ventnor

NJ060: May 20, 2019, Ship Bottom

LOCATION INDEX

Absecon	July 6, 1842	NJSAF #01
Atlantic City	July 6, 1902	NJSAF #09
	September 16, 1903	NJSAF #10
	Late August 1905	NJSAF #12
	June 30, 1916	NJSAF #16
	August 26, 1965	NJSAF #44
Bay Head	January 7, 2013	NJSAF #51
Beach Haven	July 1, 1916	NJSAF #17
Brielle	July 23, 1941	NJSAF #39
Brigantine	June 22, 1966	NJSAF #45
Camden	December 6, 2009	NJSAF #49
Cape May	June 21, 2014	NJSAF #52
Delaware Bay	August 8, 1907	NJSAF #13
Egg Harbor	July 25, 2011	NJSAF #50
Highlands	August 1886	NJSAF #03
	August 1886	NJSAF #04
	Late August 1886	NJSAF #05

Lavallette	August 27, 1913	NJSAF #15
Long Branch	June 12, 1936	NJSAF #38
Longport	August 29, 1891	NJSAF #07
Manasquan	August 12, 1961	NJSAF #43
	June 11, 2013	NJSAF #53
Mantoloking	August 19, 1932	NJSAF #36
Matawan	July 12, 1916	NJSAF #19, 20, 21, 22
Navesink	July 28, 1904	NJSAF #11
Ocean City	January 21, 1917	NJSAF #24, 25
	June 26, 1932	NJSAF #34
	August 30, 1960	NJSAF #42
	July 28, 1980	NJSAF #47
Offshore NJ	August 24, 1928	NJSAF #29
Point Pleasant	July 12, 1945	NJSAF #57
Raritan Bay	August 29, 1884	NJSAF #02
	August 2, 1895	NJSAF #08
Sandy Hook	August 6, 1931	NJSAF #32
	October 21, 1975	NJSAF #46
Sea Bright	August 17, 1880	NJSAF #06
	June 17, 1880	NJSAF #54
	June 11, 1880	NJSAF #55
	June 27, 1898	NJSAF #56
	July 13, 1916	NJSAF #58
	September 23, 1917	NJSAF #23
	Summer 1923	NJSAF #26
	July 27, 1926	NJSAF #27
	November 18, 1928	NJSAF #30
	August 27, 1931	NJSAF #33

BIBLIOGRAPHY

CHAPTER 1. 1842–1885

NJSAF #1: *New York Evening Post*, July 11, 1842.
NJSAF #55: *Red Bank Register*, June 24, 1880.
NJSAF #54: *Red Bank Register*, June 14, 1880.
NJSAF #2: *Atlantic Constitution*, August 28, 1881.

CHAPTER 2. 1886–1895

NJSAF #3: *Red Bank Register*, September 1, 1886.
NJSAF #4: *Red Bank Register*, September 1, 1886.
NJSAF #5: *Red Bank Register*, September 1, 1886.
NJSAF #6: *New York* Times, August 17, 1890.
NJSAF #7: *Daily Argus News* [Crawford, IN], September 3, 1891.
  Daily True American [Trenton, NJ], August 31, 1891.
NJSAF #8: *Boston Daily Globe*, August 3, 1895.

CHAPTER 3. 1898–1913

NJSAF #56: *Red Bank Register*, July 27, 1898.
NJSAF #9: *New York Times*, July 7, 1902.
NJSAF #10: *Indiana Messenger*, September 16, 1903.

NJSAF #11: *New York Herald Tribune*, July 29, 1904.
  New York Times, July 29, 1904.
NJSAF #12: *The Sun*, "Sharks That Attack Men," 1910.
NJSAF #13: *New Oxford Item*, August 8, 1907.
NJSAF #14: *Washington Post*, August 27, 1913.
NJSAF #15: *Belmar Coast Adviser*, August 29, 1913.
  Trenton Evening News, August 27, 1913.

CHAPTER 4. THE SUMMER OF 1916

NJSAF #16: *New York Times*, July 2, 1916
NJSAF #17: *New York Times*, July 2, 1916.
NJSAF #18: *Asbury Park Press*, July 7, 1916.
  Belmar Advisor, July 7, 1916.
  New York Times, July 7, 1916.
NJSAF #19–22: *Asbury Park Press*, June 29, 1916.
  Matawan Tribune, July 13, 1916.
  Matawan Tribune, July 20, 1916.
  New York Times, July 14, 1916.
  New York Times, July 22, 1916.
NJSAF #58: *New York Times*, July 13, 1916.

CHAPTER 5. 1917–1926

NJSAF #23: *Red Bank Register*, September 26, 1917.
NJSAF #24–25: *New York Herald Tribune*, August 23, 1960.
NJSAF #26: *New York Herald Tribune*, August 27, 1931.
NJSAF #27: American Institute Biological Science, case # 829, as reported
  in *Sharks and Survival* by Perry Gilbert.
NJSAF #28: *Washington Post*, August 26, 1926.

CHAPTER 6. 1928–1931

NJSAF #29: *Decatur Evening Herald*, August 24, 1928.
  Indiana Weekly Messenger, October 4, 1928.

NJSAF #30: *New York Herald*, November 19, 1928.
  New York Herald Tribune, November 19, 1928.
NJSAF #31: *Daily Courier* [Connellsville, PA], July 21, 1931.
NJSAF #32: *New York Times*, August 6, 1931.
NJSAF #33: *New York Herald Tribune*, August 28, 1931.

CHAPTER 7. 1932–1936

NJSAF #34: *New York Times*, June 29, 1932.
NJSAF #35: *New York Times*, June 29, 1932.
NJSAF #36: *Lime Springs Herald*, September 22, 1932.
NJSAF #37: *Hammond [IN] Times*, June 20, 1935.
  New York Times, June 19, 1935.
NJSAF #38: *New York Times*, June 13, 1936.

CHAPTER 8. 1941–1960

NJSAF #39: *New York Times*, July 23, 1941.
NJSAF #57: *Belmar Coastal Adviser*, July 13, 1945.
NJSAF #40: *Evening Star* [Washington, D.C.], August 22, 1960.
  Huntington Democrat, July 4, 2010.
NJSAF #41: *Red Bank Register*, August 23, 1960.
  Times Recorder, August 23, 1960.
NJSAF #42: *Asbury Park Press*, August 31, 1960.
  Red Bank Register, August 31, 1960.

CHAPTER 9. 1962–2000

NJSAF #43: *Manitowoc Herald Times*, August 13, 1962.
  New York Journal-American, August 14 and 15, 1962.
  New York Times, August 12, 1962.
  Red Bank Register, August 13, 1962.
NJSAF #44: *Philadelphia Inquirer*, August 27, 1965.
NJSAF #45: *Asbury Park Press*, October 22, 1975.
NJSAF #46: *Asbury Park Press*, October 22, 1975.
  Red Bank Register, October 22, 1975.
NJSAF #47: Global Shark Attack Accident File.

CHAPTER 10. 2005–2014

NJSAF #48: Associated Press release, June 8, 2005.

Eyewitness News, "NJ Shark Attack in 30 Years," June 2016.

Newsday, "Surf City Shark Attack," June 10, 2005.

New York Daily News, June 6, 2005.

Shark Blot, April 19, 2006.

NJSAF #49: Nark, Jason. "Shark-Bit at Camden Aquarium, Longtime Volunteer Diver Says Medical Bills Have Gone Unpaid and His Gig Was Deep-Sixed." *Philadelphia Inquirer*, December 17, 2010. www.inquirer.com/philly/news/20101217_Shark-bit_at_Camden_aquarium__longtime_volunteer_diver_says_medical_bills_have_gone_unpaid___his_gig_was_deep-sixed.html.

New Jersey Newsroom. "Officials Confirm Diver Was Bitten by Shark at Adventure Aquarium in Camden." April 22, 2010. www.newjerseynewsroom.com.

Shark Attack Survivors. sharkattacksurvivors.com/shark_attack/viewtopic.php?t=1364.

NJSAF #50: Araiza, Karen, and Ted Greenberg. "NJ Man's Waders Save Him from Shark Bite." NBC10 Philadelphia. July 28, 2011. www.nbcphiladelphia.com/news/local/nj-mans-waders-save-him-from-shark-bite/1908091.

NJSAF #51: *Star Ledger*. "Shark Bite Suspected in Ocean County after Teen Surfer Has Chunk Taken from Swim Fin." November 9, 2013. www.nj.com/news/2013/11/shark_bite_suspected_in_ocean_county_after_teen_surfer_has_chunk_taken_from_swim_fin.htm.

NJSAF #52: Hughes, Ryan. "Berks Couple Has Close Encounter with Great White Shark." WFMZ, 69 news, June 25, 2014. www.wfmz.com/news/area/berks/berks-couple-has-close-encounter-with-great-white-shark/article_7087af08-3416-5ad9-9ef4-950c1208be39.html.

NJSAF #53: Huffington Post. "Shark Jumps into Boat, Scares the Carp out of New Jersey Fisherman." June 11, 2013. www.huffpost.com/entry/shark-jumps-into-boat-backflipped_n_3423792.

NBC10 Philadelphia. "Shark Jumps into NJ Fishing Boat." June 7, 2013. www.nbcphiladelphia.com/news/local/Shark-Jumps-Onto-Fishing-Boat-210647241.html.

NJSAF #59: *Asbury Park Press*, August 7, 2019.

NJSAF #60: *Asbury Park Press*, August 7, 2019.

ADDITIONAL BIBLIOGRAPHY

Capuzzo, Michael. *Close to Shore*. New York: Broadway Books, 2001.

Castro, Jose I. *The Sharks of North America*. New York: Oxford University Press, 2011.

———. *The Sharks of North American Waters*. College Station: Texas A&M University Press, 1983.

Compagno, Leonard, Marc Dando and Sarah Fowler. *Sharks of the World*. Princeton, NJ: Princeton University Press, 2005.

Coppleson, Victor, and Peter Goadby. *Shark Attack*. New South Wales, AUS: Angus and Robinson Press, 1988.

Ellis, Richard. *The Book of Sharks*. New York: Alfred A. Knopf, 1996.

Ellis, Richard, and John E. McCosker. *Great White Shark*. New York: HarperCollins Publishers, 1991.

Fernicola, Richard G. *Twelve Days of Terror*. Guilford, CT: Rowman and Littlefield, 2016.

Gilbert, Perry W. *Sharks and Survival*. Lexington, MA: D.C. Heath and Company, 1975.

Healy, Joseph B. *Unspeakable Horror*. New York: Skyhorse Publishing, 2017.

McCormick, Harold W., Tom Allen and William E. Young. *Shadows in the Sea*. New York: Scarborough Books, 1978.

Moss, Sanford A. *Sharks: An Introduction for the Amateur Naturalist*. Englewood Cliffs, NJ: Prentice-Hall, 1984.

Russell, Jesse, and Ronald Chon. *Jersey Shore Shark Attacks of 1916*. Edinburgh, Scotland: LENNEX Corp., 2012.

Schnitzspahn, Karen L. *Jersey Shore Food History*. Charleston, SC: The History Press, 2012.

ABOUT THE AUTHORS

Local shore residents Patricia and Robert Heyer combine their mutual love of research with his biological background and her love of local history and storytelling in their recent title, *Shark Attacks of the Jersey Shore: A History*. They can be reached at heyerwriter@gmail.com.